EN CONTEXTE

A1

EXERCICES DE VOCABULAIRE

Anne Akyüz
Bernadette Bazelle-Shahmaei
Joëlle Bonenfant
Marie-Françoise Orne-Gliemann

hachette
FRANCAIS LANGUE ÉTRANGÈRE

Dessins
Nicolas Piroux : pages 15, 21, 23, 24, 30, 31, 33, 35, 42, 43, 46, 48, 54, 57, 58, 60, 70, 72, 78, 80, 81, 82, 92, 107, 109, 111, 115
Gabriel Rebufello : pages 20, 25, 32, 37, 44, 45, 49, 53, 54, 59, 62, 63, 76, 79, 80, 82, 94,110

Conception graphique
Couverture : Christophe ROGER
Intérieur : EIDOS

Réalisation
Mise en pages : Valérie GOUSSOT

Enregistrements audio, montage et mixage
QUALI'SONS (David HASSICI)

ISBN : 978-2-01-401642-0

© Hachette Livre 2019

58, rue Jean Bleuzen, CS 70007, 92178 Vanves Cedex

www.hachettefle.com

15 **Répondez aux devinettes de Roxane.**

Ex. : – Quel jour est avant le vendredi ? – C'est le jeudi.

1. – Après le samedi ? – C'est le ....

2. – Avant le jeudi ? – C'est le ....

3. – Avant le mercredi ? – C'est le ....

4. – Après le dimanche ? – C'est le ....

5. – Après le vendredi ? – C'est le ....

6. – Avant le samedi ? – C'est le ....

16 **Écrivez les mots.**

Hier • week-end • semaine • Aujourd'hui • Demain

Ex. : La semaine commence le lundi et finit le dimanche.

1. Il y a deux jours dans le w................- e................ : le samedi et le dimanche.

2. A........................, vendredi 15 mars, je termine mon travail. D........................, je pars en voyage.

H........................, jeudi 14 mars, j'ai acheté mes billets de train.

17 **Lisez les phrases. Cochez *vrai* ou *faux*.**

	vrai	faux
Ex. : Une semaine a 7 jours.	✔	
1. Aujourd'hui, c'est après hier.		
2. Mardi n'est pas un jour du week-end.		
3. Aujourd'hui c'est jeudi ; demain c'est vendredi.		
4. Dimanche est le premier jour du week-end.		
5. Demain, c'est mercredi; hier c'était lundi.		
6. Hier, c'est avant aujourd'hui.		

014 **18** **Écoutez et complétez.**

Ex. : Paul va au cinéma vendredi soir.

1. Ma sœur arrive .... **(1)**.

2. Le magasin est fermé le .... **(2)**.

3. Ce .... **(3)**, nous partons à la campagne.

4. Le .... **(4)** et le .... **(5)**, je vais à la piscine.

5. Vous venez .... **(6)** ? Très bien.

6. Elle part à Berlin pendant une .... **(7)**.

BILAN

1 **Remplissez la grille.**

1. Arrivées et départs des trains
2. 60 secondes
3. Sept jours
4. Avant vendredi
5. de 7h 00 à midi
6. 60 minutes
7. 00h 00
8. Après mardi

2 **Madame Mourier prend rendez-vous chez le médecin. Écoutez et complétez le dialogue.**

– Bonjour monsieur, je téléphone pour un rendez-vous avec le docteur Delorme.

– Oui, pour quand ?

– .... **(1)**, c'est possible ?

– Ce .... **(2)**, le docteur n'est pas là. Mais cet .... **(3)**, c'est possible.

– .... **(4)** ?

– À 15 .... **(5)**, ça va ?

– Oui, très bien

– Vous êtes madame ?

– Madame Mourier.

– Bien merci. À tout à l'heure, madame Mourier.

3 **Sabrina appelle le magasin pour connaître les horaires. Complétez le dialogue.**

après-midi • heures • horaires • samedi • matin • soir

– Allô, bonjour, quels sont les .... **(1)** d'ouverture du magasin ?

– Le .... **(2)**, nous sommes ouverts de 9 .... **(3)** à midi.

Et l'... **(4)**, de 14h00 à 19h00. Le jeudi .... **(5)**, nous fermons à 20h30.

– Et le week-end, le magasin est ouvert ?

– Le .... **(6)** oui, mais pas le dimanche.

– Je vous remercie.

La famille **3**

> Pour décrire la situation familiale

> Pour nommer les membres de la famille

A La situation de famille

 1 Lisez et écoutez les mots.

un copain / une copine	célibataire
un couple	divorcé
la femme	marié
le mari	pacsé
	séparé
vivre avec	veuf / veuve
vivre seul	
vivre en couple = ensemble	

2 Mettez les lettres dans l'ordre pour retrouver les mots.

Ex. : p e o n i c : J'ai une copine.

1. o l c u p e : Nous vivons en ....

2. r é a m i : Je suis .... avec Aline.

3. b i a t e c a l é i r : Cécile est ....

4. i c n o p a : Astrid a un ....

5. m e f m e : Je vous présente ma ....

6. v é c o d r i : Tu es .... ?

7. v e e v u : Marie est ....

3 Associez les phrases de même sens.

1. La vie commune d'Éric et d'Éléna est terminée.   a. Il est veuf.
2. Amir n'est pas marié.   b. Ils sont séparés.
3. La femme d'Adrien est morte.   c. Il est célibataire.
4. Je suis en couple.   d. Je ne vis pas seul.
5. Paul et Emma vivent ensemble.   e. Je suis la femme d'Alex.
6. Alex est mon mari.   f. Is sont pacsés.

4 Écoutez et complétez.

Ex : C'est Frank, mon copain.

1. Voici mon .... , Antoine.

2. Elle est .... ?

3. Tu es la .... de Thomas ?

4. Vous êtes un .... jeune !

5. Lucie, c'est ta .... ?

6. Elle va .... avec Akim.

7. Monsieur Alliot, vous êtes .... ?

B Les membres de la famille

018 **5** **Lisez et écoutez les mots.**

les enfants	la fille
la famille	le fils
la mère	le frère
les parents	le grand-père
le père	la grand-mère
	la sœur

6 **Complétez.**

~~parents~~ • fils • mère • enfants • fille • père

Ex. : les parents

1. le p............................ **2.** la f............................ **3.** le f............................ **4.** la m............................

5. les e............................

7 **Classez les membres de la famille dans le tableau.**

~~la mère~~ • la fille • le frère • la grand-mère • le père • le fils • le grand-père • la sœur

une femme	un homme
Ex. : la mère	**4.** ....
1.	**5.** ....
2.	**6.** ....
3.	**7.** ....

8 **Associez les membres de la famille (masculins avec féminins).**

1. le père   •   •   **a.** la sœur
2. le frère   •   •   **b.** la mère
3. le grand-père   •   •   **c.** la femme
4. le fils   •   •   **d.** la grand-mère
5. le mari   •   •   **e.** la fille

9 **Regardez le dessin et complétez.**

parents • père • mère • fils • fille • enfants • frère • sœur • grand-mère • grand-père

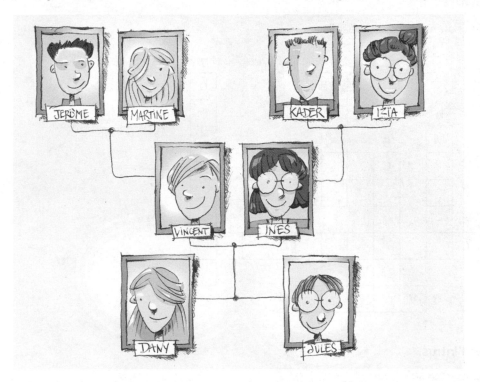

Ex. : Inès est la fille de Kader et d'Izia.

1. Jules est le .... de Dany.

2. Vincent est le .... de Jules et de Dany.

3. Martine et Jérôme sont les .... de Vincent.

4. Dany est la .... de Jules.

5. Kader est le .... et Izia est la .... de Dany et de Jules.

6. Vincent est le .... de Martine et de Jérôme.

7. Izia est la .... d'Inès.

8. Jules et Dany sont les .... de Vincent et d'Inès.

10 **Écoutez les informations sur la famille de Dany et de Jules (exercice 8). Cochez *vrai* ou *faux*.**

	Ex.	1	2	3	4	5
vrai	✔					
faux						

1 **Lisez les phrases et remplissez la grille.**

1. Arthur et moi formons un … .

2. Mon frère n'est pas marié. Il est … .

3. Mon grand-père est mort. Ma grand-mère est … .

4. Stéphanie et moi vivons ensemble. Je suis … avec elle.

5. La … de mon frère s'appelle Virginie.

6. Sophie est ma … .

7. Mes parents sont séparés. Ils sont … .

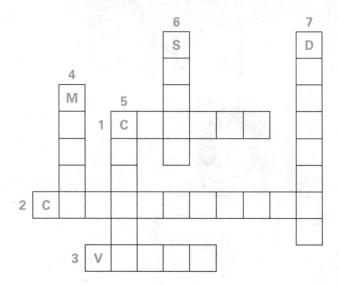

2 **Barrez l'intrus.**

1. marié – pacsé – veuf

2. mère – fille – copain

3. séparé – marié – divorcé

4. célibataire – mari – femme

5. frère – sœur – copine

6. vivre seul – vivre en couple – vivre ensemble

7. grand-père – grand-mère – fils

3 **Écoutez et soulignez l'information correcte.**

1. Je suis le mari d'Isabelle. Je suis le père d'Isabelle.

2. On vit en couple. On est divorcés.

3. Maylis est la fille de ma mère. Maylis est la fille de ma fille.

4. Je suis la sœur de Jordan. Je suis la fille de Jordan.

5. Mes parents vivent ensemble. Mes parents ne vivent pas ensemble.

6. Mon fils n'est pas marié. Mon fils est marié.

7. Ilian et Éloïse sont frère et sœur. Ilian et Éloïse sont mari et femme.

La vie quotidienne

❯ Pour parler de ses activités quotidiennes   ❯ Pour nommer les objets de la toilette

A Les activités quotidiennes

 1 **Lisez et écoutez les mots.**

déjeuner	prendre le petit déjeuner
dîner	se coucher ≠ se lever
dormir	se réveiller
faire les courses	travailler
faire la cuisine	
faire le ménage	

2 **Écrivez les mots.**

prend son petit déjeuner • couche • travaillent • dort • lève • ~~réveille~~

Ex. : Il se réveille.

1. Il se l.. .

2. Elle p.. .

3. Elle se c.. .

4. Il d.. .

5. Ils t.. .

3 **Mettez dans l'ordre les activités de la journée de Nicolas.**

.... Il se lève.   .... Il prend son petit déjeuner.

.... Il dîne.   ...1.... Il se réveille.

.... Il dort.   .... Il travaille.

.... Il se couche.

4 **Écrivez les mots.**

~~fait les courses~~ • dînent • fait le ménage • déjeunent • fait la cuisine

Ex. : Elle fait les courses.

1. Il f........................ le m........................ .

2. Ils d........................ .

3. Elles d........................ .

4. Il f........................ la c........................ .

5 **Écoutez et associez.**

1. 8h30 •

2. 7h15 •

3. 23h00 •

4. 7h00 •

5. 11h00 •

6. 20h30 •

7. Minuit •

8. Midi •

9. 9h00 •

10. 13h00 •

• **a.** faire les courses

• **b.** prendre son petit déjeuner

• **c.** se lever

• **d.** déjeuner

• **e.** dîner

• **f.** faire le ménage

• **g.** dormir

• **h.** faire la cuisine

• **i.** se réveiller

• **j.** se coucher

B L'hygiène

6 **Lisez et écoutez les mots.**

une brosse à dents	se brosser les dents
le dentifrice	se coiffer
une douche	se doucher / prendre une douche
un rasoir	se laver
un savon	se raser
une serviette (de toilette)	
le shampoing	

7 **Mettez les lettres dans l'ordre pour retrouver les mots.**

Ex.: t r e v t e s i e :　　　**1.**　　　**2.**　　　**3.**　　　**4.**　　　**5.**
une serviette

1. o s v a n : un ....

2. f c i i n e d t r e : du ....

3. r a o r i s : un ....

4. s s e o r b à s t d e n : une .... à ....

5. p a m h i o n g s : du ....

8 **Écrivez les mots.**

coiffe • rase • ~~lave~~ • prend une douche • brosse les dents

Ex. : Il se lave.　　　**1.** Il p .... une d ....　　　**2.** Elle se c ....

3. Elle se b .... les d ....　　　**4.** Il se r ....

9 **Cochez.**

Ex. : On se lave avec ☑ du savon ☐ une serviette

1. On se brosse les dents avec ☐ du dentifrice ☐ un rasoir

2. On se lave les cheveux avec ☐ une serviette ☐ du shampoing

3. On se rase avec ☐ un rasoir ☐ du dentifrice

10 **Retrouvez les noms des objets utilisés pour l'hygiène.**

rasoir**shampoingdentifricesavondoucheserviette**

Ex. : le rasoir

1. le ....

2. le ....

3. le ....

4. la s..

5. la ....

11 **Remplissez la grille avec des objets utilisés pour l'hygiène.**

1.   2.   3.   4.   5.   6.

	5						
1	S	H	A	M	P	O	I	N	G
2	S						
3	D				R		
4	D					

BILAN

1 Numérotez les activités des 3 séries de mots de 1 à 4.

se laver les mains ......

faire la cuisine ......

faire les courses ......

déjeuner ......

prendre le petit déjeuner ......

se réveiller ......

se brosser les dents ......

se lever ......

dîner ......

travailler ......

dormir ......

se coucher ......

024 **2** Écoutez et entourez le mot que vous entendez.

1. se laver – se lever

2. faire la cuisine – faire les courses

3. se doucher – se coucher

4. une douche – se doucher

5. se réveiller – travailler

6. dîner – se raser

3 Complétez les messages.

déjeune • fais les courses • dentifrice • me douche • travailles

aujourd'hui

Tu es au supermarché ?   16:22 ✓✓

Oui, je .... 😊   16:23 ✓✓

hier

On .... ensemble ? 11:00 ✓✓

D'accord. Rendez-vous à midi.   11:01 ✓✓

Tu .... demain ? 17:36 ✓✓

Oui, je vais au bureau à 9 heures. 17:38 ✓✓

jeudi

Tu peux acheter du .... ? 18:02 ✓✓

D'accord ! 😊   18:04 ✓✓

mercredi

Vite ! Je t'attends !   20:00 ✓✓

Excuse-moi. Je .... et j'arrive ! 20:01 ✓✓

5 Les loisirs

> Pour nommer les loisirs
> (sports, instruments de musique)

> Pour parler de ses goûts

> Pour parler des activités sportives
> et culturelles

> Pour parler de ses activités à la maison

A Les activités sportives

 1 Lisez et écoutez les mots.

le basket	la natation	la piscine	faire de
l'équitation	le running	la salle de sport	jouer à
le football	le tennis	le stade	courir
la gymnastique	le vélo		
la marche		un sport collectif	
		un sport individuel	

2 Mettez les lettres dans l'ordre pour retrouver les noms des sports.

Ex. : a f t o l b o l : le football

1. o é l v : le ....

2. n i u r n g n : le ....

3. n i t n t s e : le ....

4. a h r e m c : la ....

5. a a t t n n i o : la ....

6. a é i n i t o q u t :
l'.................................

7. k a t e b s :
le ....

8. a e g m i n y u q s t :
la ....

026 **3** **Écoutez et complétez.**

Ex. : Il aime bien le basket.

1. Tu n'aimes pas la .... ?

2. C'est super, le .... !

3. Elle n'aime pas le ....

4. Vous aimez bien le .... ?

5. Le ...., vous aimez ?

6. Ils aiment ....

4 **Ces sports sont individuels ou collectifs ? Cochez.**

	sport individuel	sport collectif
Ex. : le running	✔	
1. le tennis		
2. la marche		
3. le basket		
4. le vélo		
5. la natation		
6. le football		
7. la gymnastique		

5 **Dans quels sports doit-on courir ? Soulignez.**

1. la marche **4.** la natation **7.** le vélo
2. le football **5.** le basket **8.** l'équitation
3. le running **6.** le tennis **9.** la gymnastique

6 **Où fait-on du sport ? Écrivez les mots.**

parc • piscine • stade • salle de sport

Ex. : un parc 1. un s............ 2. une s............ 3. une p............

7 **Associez les sports et les lieux.**

1. faire du running • • **a.** à la salle de sport
2. faire de la natation • • **b.** à la piscine
3. jouer au football • • **c.** dans un parc
4. faire du basket • • **d.** dans un stade

8 **Lisez les phrases. Cochez *vrai* ou *faux*.**

	vrai	faux
Ex. : On peut courir dans un stade.	✔	
1. Nous faisons de la natation à la piscine.		
2. Vous allez dans une salle de sport pour l'équitation.		
3. Tu fais du basket à la piscine.		
4. Elle va faire de la marche dans un parc.		
5. Dans un stade, on fait du football.		

9 **Barrez les phrases incorrectes si nécessaire.**

Ex : On fait du vélo. ~~On joue au vélo~~.

1. Tu fais du football. Tu joues au football.

2. Ils font de la marche. Ils jouent à la marche.

3. Nous faisons de la natation. Nous jouons à la natation.

4. Je fais du tennis. Je joue au tennis.

5. Elle fait du basket. Elle joue au basket.

> On utilise *faire de* pour tous les sports. On utilise *jouer à* pour un sport collectif

B La musique

(027) **10** **Lisez et écoutez les mots.**

la batterie	la musique	chanter
la flûte	le musicien / la musicienne	écouter
la guitare		jouer de
l'harmonica		
le piano		
le saxophone		
le violon		

> Tu joues du piano ?

11 **Écrivez les mots.**

~~musiciens~~ • guitare • piano • violon • batterie • saxophone • flûte • harmonica

Ex. : des musiciens

1. Il joue du p...................................

2. Elle joue de la b...................................

3. Il joue de la g...................................

4. Il joue du v...................................

5. Il joue du s...................................

6. Elle joue de l'h...................................

7. Il y a une f...................................

> On utilise *jouer de* pour un instrument de musique.

12 **Écrivez les mots.**

piano • musique • joue • chante • ~~musicien~~ • harmonica

Il est musicien, il j................................... **(1)** du p................................... **(2)** et de l'h................................... **(3)**.

Elle c................................... **(4)**. Ils aiment la m................................... **(5)**.

13 **Complétez.**

Ex : Tu es musicienne ? – Oui, j'aime la m................................... .

1. – Elle joue de la b...................................? – Non, elle joue de la g................................... .

2. – Il joue de la f................................... ? – Non, lui, il joue du v................................... .

3. – Elles aiment l'h................................... ? – Non, elles aiment le s................................... .

14 **Amine et Lucie se rencontrent à un concert. Écoutez et complétez le dialogue.**

– Vous jouez du .... **(1)** ?

– Non, je fais de la .... **(2)** et mon frère de la .... **(3)**. Et vous ?

– Je ne suis pas .... **(4)** ! Je .... **(5)** seulement ! Et j'adore .... **(6)**

des concerts.

C Les sorties culturelles

029 **15** **Lisez et écoutez les mots.**

le cinéma	l'opéra	sortir
le concert	le spectacle	visiter
le musée	le théâtre	

> J'adore les concerts de rock !

16 **Retrouvez les mots pour répondre aux questions.**

Ex. : – Où est-il ?
– Il est au cinéma (MA CI NÉ)

1. – Ils vont où ?
– Ils vont à un .... (CERT CON)

2. – Elle est où ?
– Elle est à l'........................... (RA O PÉ)

3. – Vous allez où ?
– On va à un .... (TA SPEC CLE)

4. – Où sont-ils ?
– Ils sont au .... (SÉE MU)

5. – Tu vas où ce soir ?
– Je vais au .... (TRE THÉ Â)

17 **Complétez.**

opéra • théâtre • musée • spectacle • ~~sortir~~ • concerts • cinéma

Ex : On n'aime pas rester à la maison ; on préfère sortir.

1. Je vais au .... pour voir un film.

2. Ce .... de clowns est très amusant.

3. Aujourd'hui, je ne peux pas visiter le .... Il est fermé.

4. Elle aime beaucoup le .... de Molière et de Shakespeare.

5. J'adore les .... de pop music.

6. Vous venez avec moi à l'........................ voir *La Tosca* ?

D | Les activités de loisirs à la maison

(030) **18 Lisez et écoutez les mots.**

le film	écouter
le jeu vidéo	jouer
la lecture	lire
la radio	regarder
la télévision	se reposer

> Tu écoutes souvent la radio ?
> J'adore ce film !

19 Que fait-elle ? Regardez les dessins et associez.

1.

2.

3.

4.

5.

> On utilise *jouer à* pour un jeu à la maison.

- **a.** elle regarde la télévision.
- **b.** elle se repose.
- **c.** elle écoute la radio.
- **d.** elle joue à un jeu vidéo.
- **e.** elle lit.

(031) **20 Écoutez et complétez.**

Ex : Tu aimes la lecture ?

1. On peut .... le .... à la ....

2. J'aime bien ce ....

3. Nous aimons beaucoup .... la ....

4. Vous aimez .... ?

5. Elle aime ....

BILAN

1 Complétez.

collectifs • flûte • harmonica • courir • piscine • violon • fait • musiciens • chante • marche

1. Maxime adore la natation : il va à la .... le mardi et le vendredi.

2. Sarah ne fait pas de running parce qu'elle n'aime pas .... mais elle fait souvent

de la .... dans le parc.

3. Jules n'aime pas les sports .... ; donc il .... du vélo et du tennis.

4. Édouard et Lauren sont .... Édouard joue du .... et de

la .... Lauren joue de l'............................. et ....

2 Ces personnes parlent de quel type d'activités ? Écoutez et cochez.

	sorties	pratique musicale	pratique sportive
1.			
2.			
3.			
4.			
5.			
6.			

3 Complétez les dialogues.

film • cinéma • lire • sortir

– Tu veux .... **(1)** ce soir ?

– Pour aller où ?

– Au .... **(2)**. Il y a un .... **(3)** super !

– Je ne peux pas, je dois .... **(4)** un document pour préparer mon examen.

marche • individuels • sport • vélo • piano • écoute • guitare

– Tu as un .... **(5)** préféré, Sergio ?

– Oui, le .... **(6)**. Et je fais aussi de la .... **(7)**. J'aime les sports

.... **(8)**.

– Et toi, Loïc ?

– Moi, je n'aime pas le sport. J'..................... **(9)** de la musique. Je joue du .... **(10)**

et de la .... **(11)**.

se reposer • lecture • loisir

– Et vous, quel est votre .... **(12)** préféré ?

– Moi, c'est la .... **(13)**. C'est super pour .... **(14)** !

Les relations humaines **6**

> Pour parler de ses amis
> Pour parler de ses voisins
> Pour adapter les expressions aux contextes

A Les relations amicales

 1 **Lisez et écoutez les mots.**

un ami / une amie	adorer
un copain / une copine	être content(e)
un anniversaire	être ensemble
un bar	faire la fête
un cadeau	s'embrasser

2 **Écrivez les mots.**

~~amis~~ • **cadeau** • **font la fête** • **être ensemble** • **anniversaire** • **contents**

Ex. : Sophie a invité des amis.

1. Ils f................ la f................ pour

son a................ .

2. Elle ouvre un c................ .

3. Ils sont c................ d'................

....

copain • **s'embrassent** • **bar** • **copine**

4. Erwan retrouve son c................ Ali et

sa c................ Inès dans un b................ .

5. Ils s'e................ .

3 **Complétez le mél de Jérémie.**

anniversaire • cadeau • copains • faire la fête • bar

À :   les copains
Objet : la fête

Salut,

Samedi on va faire la fête ! C'est l'... **(1)** de Ludovic !

Rendez-vous au .... **(2)** de la mairie à 20h. Venez avec vos .... **(3)** !

Et un petit c.. **(4)** pour Ludovic !

Jérémie

---

034 **4** **Élise et Malika sont au café. Écoutez le dialogue et complétez.**

– On va au bar des artistes ce soir ?

– Bonne idée ! J'.............................. ce **(1)** .... **(2)** ! Avec qui ?

– Avec mes .... **(3)**, tu connais Rose, Lucas et Hiroko.

– Oui, avec Lucas, on va .... **(4)** !

– Oui. Viens avec ta .... **(5)** Maria, si elle peut.

– Je suis sûr qu'elle va être .... **(6)**.

B Les relations formelles

035 **5** **Lisez et écoutez les mots.**

une fête	apporter
une invitation	être invité
un voisin / une voisine	recevoir

6 **Écrivez les mots.**

~~invitation~~ • apportent • voisin • voisine • reçoit

1. Mme Leblanc r............................... des voisins.

2. Un v...............................

3. Une v...............................

4. Les voisins a............................... des fleurs.

Ex. : une invitation

7 Complétez l'invitation de Gabrielle et Nicolas.

fête • apporter • ~~voisins~~ • invités

Nous sommes vos nouveaux voisins.

Nous organisons une _____ **(1)** pour faire connaissance.

Vous êtes _____ **(2)** Samedi à 20 heures.

Vous pouvez _____ **(3)** des gâteaux ou des boissons.

Gabrielle et Nicolas

Appt 14. 1er étage

C Des expressions utiles dans les relations

036 **8** **Lisez et écoutez les mots.**

bienvenue	à bientôt	bonsoir
bonne année	à demain	coucou
bonne soirée	au revoir	salut
bon week-end	bonjour	merci

Ça va ?
Vous allez bien ?
Comment allez-vous ?
Bien, merci et vous / toi ?

9 **Regardez les dessins et écrivez les mots.**

Bonne année • ~~Bienvenue~~ • Bonne soirée • Au revoir • Salut • merci • demain • Bonjour

Ex.

1.

2.

3.

4.

5.

037 **10** **Écoutez et entourez le dialogue correct.**

Ex. **a** – Bonjour ! – Salut, ça va ? **b** – Bonsoir ! – Salut, ça va ?

1. **a** – Au revoir ! – Au revoir, à demain ! **b** – Au revoir ! – Salut, à demain !

2. **a** – Coucou Aline ! – Ah, bonjour Mathilde ! **b** – Coucou Aline ! – Ah, salut Mathilde !

3. **a** – Bonne soirée madame Truche ! **b** – Bonne soirée madame Truche !

    – Bonne soirée madame Diot ! – Bonsoir madame Diot !

4. **a** Comment allez-vous ? – Bien merci. **b** Vous allez bien ? – Oui merci.

11 **Les personnes expriment des salutations ou des souhaits ? Cochez.**

	salutations	souhaits
Ex. : Bonjour !	✔	
1. Bonsoir.		
2. Bonne soirée.		
3. Bon week-end !		
4. Salut !		
5. Bienvenue !		
6. Au revoir.		
7. À bientôt.		
8. Bonne année !		

12 **Barrez l'intrus.**

Ex. : J'arrive, je dis : Bonjour – Coucou – ~~Au revoir~~

1. Je pars, je dis : Au revoir – Bonjour – Salut

2. On arrive, on dit : Bonjour – À demain – Salut

3. Tu pars en week-end, je dis : Au revoir – Bon week-end – Bonjour

4. Je vais dormir, tu dis : Bienvenue – Bonne nuit – À demain

5. Tu vas au théâtre ce soir, je dis : Bonne journée – Bonne soirée – Au revoir

6. Je téléphone à une copine, je dis : Au revoir – Coucou – Bonjour

13 **Associez.**

1. Au revoir •

2. Bonjour •

3. Coucou •   • **a.** relations amicales

4. Salut •   • **b.** relations formelles

5. À demain •   • **c.** relations amicales et relations formelles

6. Comment allez-vous ? •

7. Bien, et vous ? •

BILAN

1 **Lisez les phrases et remplissez la grille.**

```
            7
            □
      1 C □ □ □ □
  5       6
2 A □ □ □ □ □ □ □ □ □ □
  □         □
  □         □      3 R □ □ □ □ □ □
  Z         □
            □
4 A □ □ □
```

1. Je vais au cinéma avec ma

   ....

2. Je suis né le 29 novembre, c'est le jour

   de mon ....

3. Je vais .... mes amis chez moi.

4. J'aime beaucoup Rebecca et Silvio,

   ce sont mes ....

5. Bonjour, vous .... bien ?

6. Dans mon immeuble, je connais

   tous mes ....

7. Le matin, on dit « Bonjour » et le soir,

   on dit ....

2 **Voici le début d'un film. Soulignez le mot correct.**

Antoine et Nadia sont avec un groupe *d'amis / de cadeaux* **(1)** dans un *bar / bureau* **(2)** ;

Ils *fêtent / invitent* **(3)** l'*anniversaire / fête* **(4)** de leur *copine / copain* **(5)** Mario.

Des *fêtes / collègues* **(6)** arrivent, ils *s'embrassent / adorent* **(7)** et sont *invités / contents*

d'être ensemble **(8)**.

3 **Écoutez et complétez le dialogue.**
(038)

> **faire la fête • invités • Bonne soirée • l'anniversaire • à demain**

– Demain, on va .... **(1)** au bureau !

– Bonne idée, pourquoi ?

– C'est .... **(2)** du directeur, et tous les collègues sont

  .... **(3)**

– Bien. .... **(4)** et .... **(5)**.

4 **Complétez les dialogues.**

> **ça va • invite • Salut • ensemble**

– .... **(1)**, ... **(2)** ?

– Oui, bien !

– On va au cinéma .... **(3)** ? Je t'.................... **(4)** !

– Super, d'accord.

> **apporter • voisins • fête • Bonne journée !**

– Samedi, c'est la .... **(5)** des .... **(6)**.

– Oui ! Je vais .... **(7)** un gâteau.

– C'est gentil. .... **(8)**.

7 L'être humain

> ❯ Pour nommer les parties du corps
> ❯ Pour indiquer les positions et les mouvements du corps
> ❯ Pour faire la description physique d'une personne
> ❯ Pour indiquer le poids et la taille d'une personne

A Le corps

039 **1** **Lisez et écoutez les mots.**

Les parties du corps

le bras	le genou	le pied
le corps	la jambe	la tête
le doigt	la main	le ventre
le dos		

2 **Écrivez les mots.**

bras • doigt • ~~dos~~ • genou • jambe • main • pied • tête • ventre

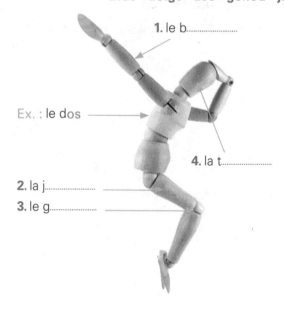

1. le b.............

Ex. : le dos

4. la t.............

2. la j.............

3. le g.............

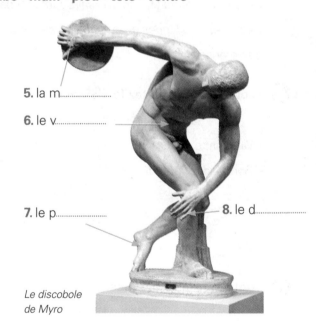

5. la m.............

6. le v.............

7. le p.............

8. le d.............

Le discobole de Myro

3 **Écrivez les parties du corps (→↓).**

C	N	A	J	P	I	E	D
V	O	X	A	G	R	B	X
E	K	Y	M	E	T	R	C
N	I	U	B	N	I	A	M
T	E	T	E	O	S	S	N
R	U	S	W	U	O	C	Y
E	Z	D	O	S	S	E	D
E	N	I	M	A	I	N	E
L	O	R	T	F	I	G	J
X	A	P	D	O	I	G	T

Horizontalement →

Ex. : pied

1. ....

2. ....

3. ....

4. ....

Verticalement ↓

5. ....

6. ....

7. ....

8. ....

4 **Entourez la phrase correcte.**

Ex. 1. 2. 3.

4. 5. 6. 7.

Ex. : Il dit « au revoir » avec la main. Il dit « au revoir » avec le doigt.

1. Elle a les pieds sur une chaise. Elle a les genoux sur une chaise.

2. Elle a la jambe cassée. Elle a le bras cassé.

3. Elle compte avec les doigts. Elle compte avec les pieds.

4. Il tourne la tête. Il tourne le corps.

5. Elle porte un sac sur la jambe. Elle porte un sac sur le dos.

6. Il a mal au ventre. Il a mal au pied.

7. Il a un bébé dans les bras. Il a un bébé dans les mains.

5 **Lisez et écoutez les mots.** `040`

Les mouvements et les actions	
baisser	être assis
courir	être couché
dessiner	être debout
écrire	s'asseoir
lever	se coucher
marcher	se lever
tenir	

6 **Écrivez les verbes.**

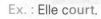

lève • dessine • tient • ~~court~~ • marchent • écrit • baisse

Ex. : Elle court.

1. Il d...........................

2. Elles m...........................

3. Il t............... la main de l'enfant.

4. Il é........................... un mèl.

5. Elle l............... et b............ les bras.

7 **Avec quelles parties du corps on fait ces actions ? Cochez. (Deux réponses sont possibles.)**

	bras et mains	jambes et pieds
Ex. : tenir	✔	
1. courir		
2. dessiner		
3. écrire		
4. marcher		
5. lever		
6. baisser		

8 **Écrivez les mots.**

debout • couché • assis • assoit • lève • ~~couche~~

Ex. : Il se couche.

1. Il est c...........................

2. Il est d...........................

3. Il s'a.. **4.** Il est a.. **5.** Il se l..

9 **Complétez.**

debout • assis • ~~se lever~~ • se coucher • couché • s'asseoir

Ex. : Il est assis et il veut être debout. Il doit se lever.

1. Il est debout et il veut être .... Il doit s'asseoir.

2. Il est assis et il veut être .... Il doit se lever.

3. Il est assis et il veut être couché. Il doit ....

4. Il est couché et il veut être assis. Il doit ....

5. Il est assis et il veut être .... Il se couche.

B La tête

041 **10** **Lisez et écoutez les mots.**

la bouche	le nez	écouter
les cheveux	l'œil/les yeux	embrasser
les dents	l'oreille	goûter
la langue	la tête	manger
		parler
		regarder
		respirer

11 **Écrivez les mots.**

bouche • cheveux • dents • langue • nez • ~~œil~~ • oreille

Ex. : un œil

1. une o..

2. la b..

3. les c..

4. le n..

5. les d..

6. la l..

12 **Retrouvez les mots.**

cheveuxœilnezoreillebouchelanguedentsyeux

Ex. : les cheveux

1. un ....

2. le ....

3. une ....

4. la ....

5. la ....

6. les ....

7. les ....

13 **Associez les objets et les parties de la tête.**

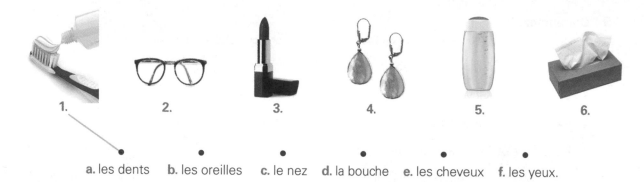

1.   **2.**   **3.**   **4.**   **5.**   **6.**

a. les dents   **b.** les oreilles   **c.** le nez   **d.** la bouche   **e.** les cheveux   **f.** les yeux.

14 **Écrivez les mots.**

embrasser • écouter • regarder • goûter • ~~respirer~~ • parler • manger

Ex. : respirer.   **1.** é......................................   **2.** r......................................   **3.** p......................................

4. e......................................   **5.** m......................................   **6.** g......................................

15 **Lisez les phrases et remplissez la grille.**

1. J'écoute avec les …
2. Je dis « oui » ou « non » avec la …
3. Je respire avec le …
4. Je regarde avec les …
5. Je parle avec la …
6. Je goûte avec la …

C La description physique

042 **16** **Lisez et écoutez les mots.**

L'apparence physique	
jeune ≠ vieux / vieille	**La taille**
grand(e) ≠ petit(e)	mesurer/faire 1 m 70
gros / grosse ≠ mince	**Le poids**
	peser / faire 55 kilos

Quelle est votre taille ?
Vous mesurez combien ?
Quel est votre poids ?
Vous pesez combien ?

17 **Écrivez les mots.**

jeune • vieille • ~~grand~~ • petit • gros • mince

Ex. : Il est grand et
son ami est p……………… .

1. La femme est
v……………… .

2. L'homme est g………………,
son ami est m……………… .

3. La fille est j……………… .

18 **Associez. (Deux réponses sont possibles.)**

1. Quelle est votre taille ? •
2. Tu fais combien ? •
3. Vous pesez combien ? •
4. Quel est votre poids ? •
5. Il mesure combien ? •

• **a.** 75 kilos
• **b.** 1 mètre 80

19 **Soulignez le verbe correct. (Deux réponses sont possibles.)**

Ex. : Il _mesure_ / a 1 mètre 75.

1. Vous _avez_ / _pesez_ combien ?

2. Il _mesure_ / _fait_ 2 mètres.

3. Elle _fait_ / _a_ 34 kilos.

4. Tu _pèses_ / _mesures_ combien ?

043 **20** **Lisez et écoutez les mots.**

Les cheveux	Les yeux
blancs	bleus
blonds	marron
bruns	verts
courts	
longs	
roux	

21 **Qui est qui ? Lisez et écrivez le nom des personnes sous les dessins.**

Aymeric a les yeux bleus et les cheveux blancs.

Daphné a les cheveux blonds et longs.

Louis a les cheveux roux et courts.

José a les yeux verts et les cheveux bruns.

Chloé a les cheveux noirs et les yeux marron.

Ex. : Aymeric   1. _____   2. _____   3. _____   4. _____

22 **Barrez les descriptions impossibles.**

Ex. : ~~Les yeux longs~~

1. Les cheveux vieux

2. Les cheveux bruns

3. Les yeux blancs

4. Les yeux marron

5. Les yeux blonds

6. Les cheveux roux

7. Les yeux courts

8. Les cheveux gros

9. Les cheveux courts

10. Les cheveux blancs

BILAN

044 **1** Écoutez et cochez.

	1	2	3	4	5	6	7	8	9	10	11	12
le corps												
la tête												

2 Répondez aux devinettes !

Devinettes

Qu'est-ce que c'est ?

1 Ils sont sur la tête, bruns ou blonds : les ....

2 Normalement, on a 32 .... dans la bouche.

3 Il y a .... aux mains.

4 Ils sont marron, noirs, verts, ou bleus : les ....

5 Avec elles, je marche ou je cours : les ....

3 Soulignez la phrase qui décrit la photo.

1. Il court. – Il marche.

2. Elle écoute. – Elle parle.

3. Elle est assise. – Elle est debout.

4. Il dessine. – Il écrit.

5. Elle lève les bras. – Elle baisse les bras.

6. Il écoute. – Il regarde.

045 **4** Des candidats répondent à l'annonce de *Beaux Films Production*. Est-ce qu'ils correspondent à l'annonce ? Écoutez et cochez.

> 🎬 **Beaux Films Productions**
> **Recherche acteurs ou actrices pour un film**
> Taille : **1m60 – 1m80**
> Poids : **50 kgs – 80 kgs**
> Cheveux : **toutes les couleurs**
> Yeux : **bleus ou verts**

	Candidat 1	Candidate 2	Candidat 3	Candidat 4	Candidat 5	Candidate 6
Oui						
Non						

8 La santé

> ❯ Pour décrire un état physique
> ❯ Pour nommer les professions et les lieux de santé

A Les maladies

 1 Lisez et écoutez les mots.

avoir de la fièvre
avoir un rhume
avoir mal à
être malade
prendre un médicament

Qu'est-ce qui ne va pas ?
Vous avez mal où ?

2 Écrivez les mots.

~~malade~~ • fièvre • prend un médicament • rhume • avoir mal à

Ex. : Il est malade.

1. Il a de la f... .

2. Il p...
un m... .

3. Il a un r... .

4. Il a m...
au d... .

3 **Qui parle ? La malade ou le médecin ? Classez.**

1. Vous êtes malade ?
2. J'ai mal au pied.
3. Elle a de la fièvre ?
4. Vous avez mal où ?
5. J'ai mal à la tête.
6. Vous avez mal au ventre ?
7. Qu'est-ce qui ne va pas ?
8. J'ai très mal aux oreilles.

la malade	le médecin
....	1. ....

4 **Vous entendez *mal* ou *malade* ? Écoutez et cochez.**

047

	Ex.	1	2	3	4	5	6
mal							
malade	✔						

5 **Soulignez la phrase correcte.**

Ex.

1.

2.

3.

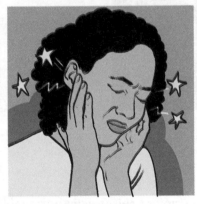

4.

5.

Ex. : On a mal au ventre. <u>On a mal à la tête</u>.

1. Elle a mal au dos. Elle est malade.
2. Tu as de la fièvre. Tu as mal au ventre.
3. Il a mal aux dents. Il a mal au ventre.
4. Elle a mal aux oreilles. Elle a mal à la jambe.
5. Elles sont malades. Elles ont mal aux dents.

B Les professions et les lieux de santé

 048 **6** **Lisez et écoutez les mots.**

Les professions	Les lieux	
le chirurgien / la chirurgienne	le cabinet médical	une analyse
le / la dentiste	l'hôpital	une consultation
l'infirmier / l'infirmière	le laboratoire	un examen
le médecin	la pharmacie	une opération
les pompiers	les urgences	une ordonnance
		une radio

7 **Écrivez les professions.**

~~dentiste~~ • médecin • pompiers • chirurgien • infirmier

Ex. : un dentiste   1. un c...................   2. un i...................

3. les p...................   4. un m...................

8 **Complétez.**

~~médecin~~ • infirmier • chirurgien • pompiers • dentiste

Ex. : Je suis malade. J'appelle le médecin.

1. J'ai mal aux dents. Je vais voir le ....

2. Il y a un accident dans la rue. On appelle les ....

3. J'ai une jambe cassée. Le .... doit faire une opération.

4. L'................... travaille dans un laboratoire.

9 **Barrez l'intrus.**

Ex. : le laboratoire – ~~le chirurgien~~ – l'analyse

1. l'hôpital – les urgences – le dentiste

2. le chirurgien – la pharmacie – les médicaments

3. le médecin – l'opération – le cabinet médical

4. les urgences – l'hôpital – le pharmacien

5. le laboratoire – l'infirmier – les pompiers

6. l'ordonnance – le médecin – l'opération

7. les pompiers – le pharmacien – les urgences

10 **Associez.**

1. Pour faire des analyses, je vais •   • **a.** à l'hôpital

2. Pour consulter un médecin, on va •   • **b.** au laboratoire

3. Pour une opération, on va •   • **c.** à la pharmacie

4. Pour acheter des médicaments, je vais •   • **d.** au cabinet médical

049 **11** **Lisez et cochez les phrases que vous entendez.**

Ex. : J'appelle les pompiers. ✔

1. L'infirmière vient ce soir.

2. Les pompiers sont là !

3. Elle va aller à l'hôpital.

4. Le cabinet médical est fermé.

5. Tu passes à la pharmacie ?

6. On ne veut pas aller chez le dentiste.

7. Il est chirurgien ou médecin ?

8. Ils doivent aller aux urgences.

12 **Les informations sont logiques ou pas ? Cochez.**

	logique	pas logique
Ex. : J'ai un rhume. Je vais chez le dentiste.		✔
1. Il est malade. Il consulte le médecin.		
2. L'infirmier travaille à la pharmacie.		
3. Le cabinet médical est à l'hôpital.		
4. Le chirurgien fait des opérations.		
5. J'ai de la fièvre. Je suis malade.		
6. Les urgences sont à l'hôpital.		

BILAN

1 Classez les phrases dans l'ordre.

Je prends les médicaments pendant 4 jours. ....

Le médecin m'examine. ....

J'ai mal au ventre. ....

Je vais au cabinet médical. ....

Le pharmacien me donne des médicaments. ....

Je vais à la pharmacie. ....

Le médecin me donne une ordonnance. ....

2 Lisez les phrases et remplissez la grille.

1. La température élevée du corps.
2. Pour avoir une ..., on prend rendez-vous au cabinet médical.
3. Il n'est pas en bonne santé, il est ....
4. Il examine le malade.
5. Je peux acheter des médicaments avec une ....
6. J'achète des médicaments dans ce magasin.
7. À l'hôpital, elle donne les médicaments au malade.

050 **3** Complétez les dialogues.

fièvre • pharmacie • médicaments • laboratoire • Qu'est-ce qui ne va pas •
analyses • cabinet • ordonnance

Au .... **(1) médical**

– Bonjour, docteur.

– Bonjour. .... **(2)** ?

– J'ai de la .... **(3)** : 39°.

À la .... **(4)**

– Bonjour, voici mon .... **(5)**

– Voilà vos .... **(6)**

– Merci.

Au .... **(7)**

– Voici le résultat de vos .... **(8)**

– Merci.

Le logement 9

> Pour décrire un logement
> Pour nommer les différentes pièces
> Pour parler de l'équipement d'un logement

A L'appartement et la maison

 1 **Lisez et écoutez les mots.**

l'appartement	la maison
l'ascenseur	la porte
l'escalier	
l'étage	ancien / ancienne ≠ neuf / neuve
la fenêtre	habiter
l'immeuble	

2 **Mettez les lettres dans l'ordre pour retrouver les mots.**

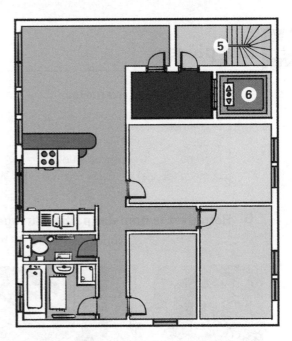

Ex. : m m l b e i u e : un immeuble

4. e n t m p p a a r e t : un ....

1. e t r p o : la ....

5. a c e e i l r s : un ....

2. r e – ê – f – t – e – n : une ....

6. r u e s s c a n e : l' ....

3. g t a e é s : les ....

3 **Johan habite ici. Lisez les phrases. Cochez *vrai* ou *faux*.**

	vrai	faux
Ex. : Johan habite une maison.	✔	
1. La maison est très ancienne.		
2. Il y a un escalier.		
3. Il y a cinq étages.		
4. On voit un ascenseur.		
5. La porte est ouverte.		
6. On voit des fenêtres.		
7. C'est une maison neuve.		

4 **Associez.**

1. Plusieurs familles habitent ensemble. •

2. Il y a généralement un ou deux étages. •   • **a.** une maison

3. On trouve des appartements. •   • **b.** un immeuble

4. Il y a souvent un ascenseur. •

B Les pièces

5 **Lisez et écoutez les mots.**

la chambre	la salle de bains
la cuisine	le séjour
la pièce	un studio
la pièce (de vie)	les toilettes / les WC

6 **Retrouvez le nom des parties du logement.**

toilettes • salle de bains • ~~cuisine~~ • chambre • séjour

Ex. : la cuisine

1. les t............................   **2.** une c............................   **3.** la s............................   **4.** le s............................

7 **Écoutez et complétez.**

1. Notre appartement a 4 pièces. Il y a 3 _____ **(1)** et un _____ **(2)**. Bien sûr,

nous avons aussi une _____ **(3)**, une _____ **(4)** et des _____ **(5)**.

2. Moi, j'ai un studio. Il n'y a pas de _____ **(6)** et pas de _____ **(7)**.

Il y a une seule _____ **(8)**, c'est la _____ **(9)**. J'ai aussi une _____ **(10)**

avec des _____ **(11)**.

8 **Qu'est-ce qu'on fait et où ? Associez. (Plusieurs réponses sont possibles.)**

1. On prépare les repas dans •

2. On dort dans •   • **a.** la cuisine

3. On se lave dans •   • **b.** la salle de bains

4. On lit dans •   • **c.** la chambre

5. On regarde la TV dans • • **d.** le séjour

6. On déjeune dans •

7. On se douche dans •

C L'équipement

 9 **Lisez et écoutez les mots.**

le canapé	l'étagère	les plaques de cuisson
la chaise	le frigo / le réfrigérateur	la table
la cuisinière	le lit	la télé / la TV
la douche	le placard	

10 **Écrivez les mots.**

~~table~~ • télévision • canapé • étagère • chaise • placard • plaques de cuisson • frigo • lit • cuisinière

Ex. : une table   **1.** une c_____   **2.** un l_____   **3.** un ca_____   **4.** un f_____

5. une é_____   **6.** un p_____   **7.** une cu_____   **8.** une t_____   **9.** les p_____

de c_____

11 **Entourez le mot correct.**

Ex. : Les assiettes sont sur (la table) / le canapé.

1. Les vêtements sont dans *le frigo* / *le placard*.

2. La salade est dans *le frigo* / sur *la chaise*.

3. Le chat est dans *la douche* / sur *le canapé*.

4. Les livres sont sur *les plaques de cuisson* / *les étagères*.

5. Le journal est sur *la table* / dans *le réfrigérateur*.

6. L'enfant est assis sur *la télé* / *la chaise*.

12 **Barrez l'intrus.**

Ex. : Dans la cuisine : ~~un lit~~ – une chaise

1. Dans le séjour : un canapé – une douche

2. Dans la chambre : un frigo – un lit

3. Dans la salle de bains : des plaques de cuisson – une douche

4. Dans la pièce de vie : une TV – les WC

5. Dans les toilettes : un réfrigérateur – une étagère

13 **Lisez les phrases et remplissez la grille.**

1. On s'assoit autour de la … pour manger.

2. Avec la …, on fait la cuisine, on prépare des gâteaux par exemple.

3. On pose des objets décoratifs ou des livres sur l'…

4. On peut s'asseoir à plusieurs sur le …

5. Pour s'asseoir à une table, il faut une …

6. On s'allonge sur le … pour dormir dans la chambre.

7. Dans la cuisine, on range les objets dans les …

8. J'allume la …pour regarder des films dans le séjour.

BILAN

1 **Complétez.**

frigo • salle de bains • cuisinière • séjour • table • chaise • douche • télé

Dans ma cuisine, il y a un
.... **(1)**, une .... **(2)**,
et une .... **(3)**.

Dans ma .... **(4)**,
il y a une .... **(5)**
et un petit placard.

Dans mon .... **(6)**,
il y a un .... **(7)**
et une grande .... **(8)**.

2 **Écoutez Léa et complétez.**

1. J'..................... dans un petit .... neuf.

2. C'est un .... : une jolie .... et une petite ....

3. Il est au troisième ....

4. J'ai une grande ....

5. J'adore mon ....

6. Il y a un ....

7. Il y a aussi une belle ....

3 **Complétez le mél de Clémence.**

cuisine • chambres • salle de bains • placards • appartement • pièce de vie •
télévision • canapé

🗑 ▪ ⟸ ⬅ ➡   👤 ▪ ⚑ ▾

À : familledíaz@hotmail.com
Objet : chez nous

Bonjour à tous,

Enfin, notre .... **(1)** est terminé. Il est super pour notre famille ! Il y a une grande

.... **(2)** avec beaucoup de .... **(3)** : je vais être très bien pour vous préparer

de bons repas. La .... **(4)** est très belle aussi avec un .... **(5)** confortable pour

regarder la .... **(6)**. Il y a aussi trois .... **(7)** et une .... **(8)**

avec une grande douche.

À bientôt,

Clémence

---

10 La ville

> Pour décrire la ville
> Pour parler des transports en ville
> Pour indiquer une direction

A Les lieux de la ville

(056) **1 Lisez et écoutez les mots.**

l'avenue	les feux	le pont
le carrefour	la mairie	le quartier
le centre-ville	le parc	la rue
le commissariat	le parking	animé ≠ calme
l'école	la place	

2 Écrivez les mots sur le dessin.

~~centre-ville~~ • quartier • pont • avenue • rue • carrefour • feux • place

Ex. : le centre-ville

1. le q.................

7. la r.................

2. la p.................

5. le p.................

4. le c.................

6. les f.................

3. l'a.................

3 **Mettez les lettres dans l'ordre pour retrouver les mots.**

Ex. : r c p a : le parc

1. r i a t m m c o s s i a :

le ....

2. g k n p r a i :

le ....

3. e r i a i m : la ....

4. l e o é c : l'...

4 **Classez les lieux de la ville dans le tableau.**

rue • quartier • école • parking • pont • place • commissariat • mairie • parc

espaces extérieurs	espaces intérieurs	espaces extérieurs ou intérieurs
rue, ...	....	....
....	....	....

5 **Complétez.**

calme • animé • école • carrefour • mairie • quartier • centre-ville • rue

– Tu habites où ?

– Dans le quartier de la .... **(1)**, c'est très tranquille, très .... **(2)**. Et toi ?

– .... **(3)** Victor Hugo, dans le .... - .... **(4)**.

Il y a une .... **(5)** et un grand .... **(6)**. C'est très .... **(7)**.

– Ah oui, je connais !

6 Lisez les phrases. Cochez *vrai* ou *faux*.

	vrai	faux
Ex. : Il y a plusieurs rues au carrefour.	✔	
1. On se promène dans un parc.		
2. Il y a du bruit dans un quartier calme.		
3. Le parking est pour les voitures.		
4. Il y a des feux aux carrefours.		
5. La mairie est un lieu pour les enfants.		
6. Une avenue est très petite.		
7. Une place est toujours ronde.		
8. Au commissariat, il y a des policiers.		

B Les transports en ville

057

7 **Lisez et écoutez les mots.**

l'arrêt de bus	le quai	le train
le billet	la station	le tramway
le bus	un taxi	pratique
la gare	un ticket	rapide
le métro	un titre de transport	

8 **Écrivez les mots.**

station (X2) • arrêt • taxi • métro • gare • ~~train~~ • bus • quai (X2)

1. – Le train est à la g................ sur le q................ n° 5.

2. Le m................ est à la s................ *Louvre*.

Il y a des gens sur le q................ .

3. Trois personnes attendent le b................

à l'................ *Bastille*.

4. Il y a un t................ à la s................ .

9 **Complétez.**

~~titre de transport~~ • train • ticket • billet

1.

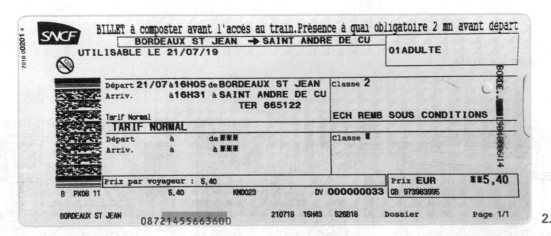

2.

1. Pour prendre un transport en ville, on doit avoir un titre de transport. Pour faire un seul voyage,

on achète un ....

2. Pour prendre le t..............................., on doit acheter un b............................... .

10 **Classez les mots.**

~~bus~~ • station de taxi • gare • tramway • train • station de métro • métro • quai • taxi • arrêt de bus

moyens de transport	lieux
bus, ...	....
....	....

11 **Associez. (Plusieurs réponses sont possibles.)**

1. une station •   • **a.** de métro
2. un arrêt •   • **b.** de train
3. un ticket •   • **c.** de bus
4. un billet •   • **d.** de taxi
                      • **e.** de tramway

12 **Entourez le mot correct.**

À Paris, je prends le (bus) / ticket ou le billet / métro **(1)** parfois le tramway.

J'ai toujours des tickets / arrêts **(2)**. Je ne prends jamais le taxi ; c'est rapide / cher **(3)**.

Le bus est pratique / cher **(4)**, mais le métro est plus rapide. Pour aller de Strasbourg à Marseille,

je prends le tramway / train **(5)**, j'achète mon ticket / billet **(6)** à l'avance.

C Les directions

058 **13 Lisez et écoutez les mots.**

à droite ≠ à gauche	continuer
tout droit	descendre
	monter
	tourner
	traverser

> Vous continuez tout droit.
> Aux feux, tu tournes à gauche.

14 Écrivez les mots.

~~descend~~ • **traverse** • **continue** • **à gauche** • **monte** • **à droite**

Ex.: Il descend du bus.

1. Il m_____ les escaliers.

2. Il prend la rue à d_____ .

3. Il c_____ tout droit.

4. Il t_____ le pont.

5. Il tourne à g_____ .

15 **Barrez la 2ème phrase si elle a un sens différent de la première.**

Ex. : Je descends les escaliers. ~~Je monte la rue~~.

1. Je tourne à droite. Je ne continue pas tout droit.

2. Je tourne à gauche. Je vais à gauche.

3. Je traverse le pont. Je ne prends pas le pont.

4. Je prends la rue à droite. Je tourne à droite.

5. Je monte les escaliers. Je reste dans la rue.

6. Je vais tout droit. Je tourne à gauche.

16 **Jérôme cherche la mairie. Associez les phrases et les numéros.**

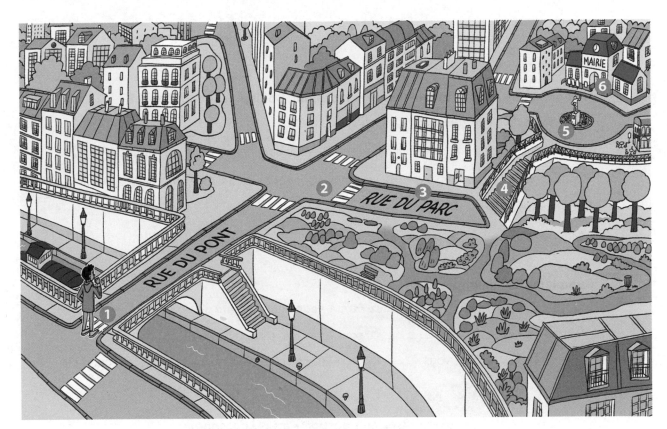

1. Vous continuez tout droit dans la rue du Parc. ......

2. Vous montez les escaliers. ......

3. C'est là. ......

4. Vous traversez le pont. 1

5. Vous tournez à droite. ......

6. Vous traversez la place.

BILAN

1 **Barrez l'intrus**

1. Je traverse : *la rue* / *le train*

2. Je monte : *les escaliers* / *le carrefour*

3. Je traverse : *le métro* / *la place*

4. Je continue : *tout droit* / *le parking*

5. Je prends : *la gare* / *le train*

6. Je tourne : *tout droit* / *à gauche*

7. Je traverse : *le pont* / *les feux*

8. Je descends : *les feux* / *la rue*

059 **2** **Deux collègues parlent des transports. Écoutez et complétez le dialogue.**

– Tu habites au .... **(1)** ?

– Non, j'habite loin, je dois prendre le .... **(2)** et le .... **(3)**. Et toi ?

– Moi, j'habite dans le nouveau .... **(4)**, près du .... **(5)**.

Je prends le .... **(6)**. C'est très .... **(7)** !

– Quelle chance !

3 **Une personne dans la rue demande son chemin. Soulignez le mot correct.**

– Pardon, je cherche *une station* / *un arrêt* **(1)** de métro.

– Alors, vous traversez *le carrefour* / *la mairie* **(2)**, vous *continuez* / *tournez* **(3)** tout droit et

vous *montez* / *tournez* **(4)** à gauche, aux feux. Vous allez voir, il y a un arrêt de *bus* / *taxis* **(5)**,

et le métro est là.

– Merci beaucoup !

4 **Complétez les dialogues.**

traversez • train • continuez • Quai

– Pardon monsieur, le .... **(1)** pour Grenoble, s'il vous plaît ?

– .... **(2)** N°4, vous .... **(3)** le hall A et vous .... **(4)** tout droit.

– Merci.

ticket • titres de transport • arrêt • descendez

– « Contrôle des .... **(5)** ! Madame, vous n'avez pas de .... **(6)** ?

Vous .... **(7)** au prochain .... **(8)** ! »

à droite • continuer tout droit • pont • rue

– Taxi !

– Bonjour.

– Bonjour monsieur, je vais .... des Écoles **(9)** s'il vous plaît. C'est loin ?

– Non, Il faut 10 minutes environ. Après le .... **(10)**, on va .... **(11)** et après

on tourne .... **(12)**. Et on y est !

Les aliments et les boissons 11

❯ Pour nommer les aliments et les boissons   ❯ Pour parler des goûts alimentaires

A Les fruits et les légumes

 1 **Lisez et écoutez les mots.**

Les fruits	Les légumes
une banane	une carotte
une cerise	un concombre
un citron	des haricots verts
une fraise	une pomme de terre
une orange	une salade
une pomme	une tomate
le raisin	

2 **Retrouvez les noms des fruits.**

citroncerisefraisebananeraisinpommeorange

Ex. : un citron   1. une o............................   2. une p............................   3. une b............................

4. une f............................   5. une c............................   6. du r............................

3 **Mettez les lettres dans l'ordre pour retrouver le nom des légumes.**

Ex.: temato : une tomate   1. lasade : une ....   2. terotca : une ....

3. mepom :

une .... de terre

4. ricotsha :

des .... verts

5. breconcom :

un ....

4 **Complétez.**

~~légumes~~ • carotte • banane • cerise • concombre • orange • pomme • haricots verts • raisin • tomate • ~~fruits~~ • salade

Ex.: les légumes

1. la ....

2. le ....

3. les ....

4. la ....

5. la ....

Les fruits

6. la ....

7. la ....

8. l'...............................

9. la ....

10. le ....

5 **Retrouvez dans la grille 5 noms de fruits et 5 noms de légumes.**

C	O	N	C	O	M	B	R	E	C
A	V	H	J	O	R	A	N	G	E
R	A	I	S	I	N	N	Z	Q	R
O	Q	F	S	A	L	A	D	E	I
T	O	M	A	T	E	N	K	J	S
T	X	P	O	M	M	E	S	H	E
E	M	H	A	R	I	C	O	T	S

Horizontalement →

Ex. : un concombre

1. une ....

2. du ....

3. une ....

4. une ....

5. des ....

6. des ....

Verticalement ↓

7. une ....

8. une ....

9. une ....

B Les boissons

(061) **6** **Lisez et écoutez les mots.**

Les boissons	avoir soif
l'alcool	boire
la bière	
le café	
l'eau	
le jus de fruit	
le lait	
le thé	
le vin	

7 **Complétez avec le nom d'une boisson.**

Ex. : J'aime les jus de fruits.

1. Je préfère le t............................... .

2. Il aime le l............................... .

3. Elle déteste le c............................... .

4. Je n'aime pas l'a............................... .

5. Je n'aime pas le v............................... .

6. Moi, j'aime la b............................... .

8 **Mettez les lettres dans l'ordre pour retrouver le nom des boissons.**

Ex. : (a e u). L'eau est la meilleure boisson.

1. Le (è h t) .... est ma boisson préférée.

2. Je n'aime pas le (n v i) .... et l'(l l o o c a) ....

3. J'adore le (é a f c) ....

4. J'adore les (s j u e d t i f r u s) ....

5. J'aime beaucoup le (i t a l) ....

9 **Trois amis sont au café. Écoutez et soulignez le mot correct.** (062)

– Bonjour, vous désirez *un thé* / *un café* ?

– *Un café* / *Un thé*, s'il vous plaît.

– Pour moi, *un thé* / *un café* et *du vin* / *de l'eau.*

– Et pour moi, *une bière* / *un jus de fruit.*

– Très bien !

10 **Thierry et Sandrine parlent de leurs goûts. Complétez le dialogue.**

café • thé • eau • bois • jus de fruits • bière • ~~alcool~~ • soif

– L'alcool, tu aimes ?

– En général, non. Je .... **(1)** une .... **(2)** quand j'ai très .... **(3)**. Et toi ?

– Non, je préfère le .... noir **(4)** ou le .... **(5)**. Et j'aime aussi les .... **(6)**.

Mais, pour moi, le mieux, c'est l'............... **(7)** !

C Autres aliments

11 **Lisez et écoutez les mots.** (063)

La viande	le fromage	le chocolat
le bœuf	un œuf / des œufs	le pain
le mouton	les pâtes	le poivre
le porc	le poisson	le sel
le poulet	le riz	le sucre
		avoir faim
		manger

12 **Mettez les lettres dans l'ordre pour retrouver les mots.**

Ex.: un foebu :
un bœuf

1. un tonmou :
un ....

2. un ssonoip :
un ....

3. un telpou
un ....

4. un ocrp
un ....

 67

13 **Regardez les photos et complétez les phrases.**

pâtes • pain • sucre • chocolat • fromage • poivre • riz • sel • œufs

Ex. : Vous aimez les pâtes ?

1. Ici, le f_ _ _ _ _ _ est fort !

2. Tu veux du s_ _ ?

3. Il y a trop de p_ _ _ _ _ .

4. Je mets du s_ _ _ _ dans mon café.

5. J'adore les o_ _ _ _ .

6. Je mange beaucoup de p_ _ _ .

7. Nous adorons le r_ _, et vous ?

8. Tu veux un morceau de c_ _ _ _ _ _ _ ?

Ex.   1.   2.

3.   4.   5.

6.   7.   8.

064 **14** **Soulignez la phrase que vous entendez.**

Ex. : Du sel, pas beaucoup, s'il te plaît ! / Du sucre, pas beaucoup, s'il te plaît !

1. Oui, un œuf, je veux bien ! / Oui, du bœuf, je veux bien !

2. Non merci, pas de poivre ! / Non merci, pas de porc !

3. J'adore le pain ! / J'adore les pâtes !

4. Il y a trop de sel ! / Il y a trop de sucre !

5. Je n'aime pas le pain blanc. / Je n'aime pas le riz blanc.

15 **Barrez l'aliment qui ne convient pas.**

Ex. : Sur les tomates : *sucre* ou *sel* ?

1. Sur les haricots : *poivre* ou *chocolat* ?

2. Dans le yaourt : *sucre* ou *pain* ?

3. Dans les pâtes : *fromage* ou *riz* ?

4. Sur le bœuf : *œufs* ou *poivre* ?

5. Sur les œufs : *sel* ou *poisson* ?

6. Avec le poisson : *riz* ou *chocolat* ?

065 **16** **Élodie est au restaurant universitaire. Elle parle avec le cuisinier. Écoutez et complétez.**

– Bonjour, on mange quoi aujourd'hui ?

– Du .... **(1)** avec des haricots verts.

– Oh, j'ai très .... **(2)** ! Je peux aussi avoir du .... **(3)** !

– Bien sûr. Il y a des .... **(4)** aussi.

– Et des pommes de terre ?

– Non. Demain, avec du .... **(5)** !

– Et on a du .... **(6)** ?

– Bien sûr ! Et aussi une crème au .... **(7)**. Bon appétit !

– Merci.

1 Regardez les photos et complétez le message de madame Dubois.

1.
2.
3.
4.
5.
6.
7.
8.
9.

S'il te plaît, pour le repas de ce soir, achète des t............................ **(1)**, un p............................ – roti **(2)** et des

h...................... v...................... Prends aussi du l...................... **(4)**, du c...................... **(5)**, des o...................... **(6)** et du

s.................. **(7)** pour le gâteau. Prends aussi des f.................. **(8)**. Et n'oublie pas le p.................. **(9)** ! Merci ! ☺

2 Classez les aliments.

pain • tomate • poulet • banane • fraise • sucre • carotte • porc • sel • vin • thé • haricots verts •
lait • œufs • café • poivre • citron • mouton • cerise • concombre • bœuf • eau • pomme • salade

fruits	légumes	boissons	viandes	autres aliments

066 **3** Alma organise une fête et demande à ses amis de choisir ce qu'ils veulent manger.
Écoutez les réponses et complétez son tableau.

	poisson	poulet	riz	haricots verts	gâteau au chocolat	fraises	vin	eau
Odile								
Didier								
Caroline								
Émile								
Béatrice								
Frédo								
Gustave								

12 Les repas à la maison et au restaurant

❯ Pour parler des repas
❯ Pour nommer les objets de la table

❯ Pour communiquer au restaurant

A Les repas et la table

 1 **Lisez et écoutez les mots.**

Les repas	La table
le déjeuner	une assiette
le diner	une bouteille
le petit déjeuner	un couteau
	une cuillère / une petite cuillère
déjeuner	une fourchette
dîner	un plat
prendre le petit déjeuner	une serviette
	une tasse
	un verre

2 **Associez. (Plusieurs réponses sont possibles.)**

1. Il est 7h00 du matin. •

2. Il est midi. •

3. Il est 19h30. •

a. C'est l'heure de déjeuner.

b. Je prépare le petit déjeuner pour la famille.

c. Nous déjeunons au restaurant.

d. C'est l'heure de dîner.

e. Issam et Morgan vont dîner chez des amis.

f. Je prends mon premier repas de la journée.

3 **Écrivez les mots.**

assiette • petite cuillère • couteau • verre • plat • serviette • ~~cuillère~~ •
fourchette • bouteille

Ex. : une cuillère

1. un c...........................

2. une a...........................

3. une f...........................

4. une p........................... c...........................

5. un p...........................

6. un v...........................

7. une s...........................

8. une b...........................

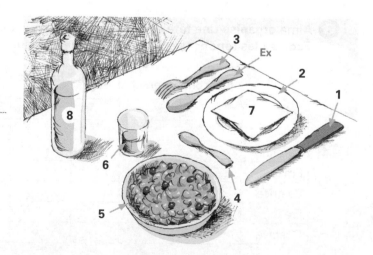

4 **Associez.**

Ex. : une fourchette

1. une assiette

2. une cuillère

3. une bouteille   **a.** pour boire

4. un plat   **b.** pour manger

5. un couteau

6. un verre

7. une tasse

Ex.	1	2	3	4	5	6	7
b							

068 **5** **Écoutez. Rahim demande à Maria comment il doit préparer la table pour le dîner. Soulignez la phrase que vous entendez.**

Ex. : **a.** Je vais préparer la table. **b.** Je vais préparer le repas.

1. **a.** On met quelles fourchettes ? **b.** On met quelles cuillères ?

2. **a.** Les serviettes rouges ? **b.** Les assiettes rouges ?

3. **a.** Les couteaux, à droite ou à gauche ? **b.** Les verres, à droite ou à gauche ?

4. **a.** Je mets des petites cuillères ? **b.** Je mets des tasses ?

5. **a.** Tu veux une assiette ronde ? **b.** Tu veux un plat rond ?

6 **Retrouvez les mots des objets de la table et des repas.**

platdînerfourchettecuillèredéjeunerverrecouteaurepasassietteserviette

Ex. : un plat

1. le ....

2. une ....

3. une ....

4. le ....

5. un ....

6. un ....

7. un ....

8. une ....

9. une ....

B Le restaurant

069 **7** **Lisez et écoutez les mots.**

une addition   boire
une boisson   manger
la carte   payer
le dessert   réserver
une entrée
le menu
un plat
la table

Et comme boisson ?
Vous prenez un dessert ?
Je peux avoir l'addition ?

8   Écrivez les mots sur le dessin.

plat • ~~menu~~ • dessert • entrée

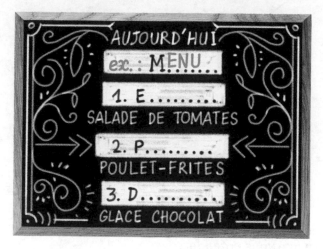

9   Complétez.

mangent • réserve une table • addition • ~~carte~~ • boivent

Ex. : Ils regardent la carte.   **1.** Ils m_____ .   **2.** Ils b_____ .

3. Il r_____ une _____ au restaurant.   **4.** Elle paie l'a_____ .

10   Aurélie et Maya veulent aller au restaurant. Écoutez et complétez le dialogue.

– On va au restaurant ce soir ?

– D'accord. Je _____ **(1)** une _____ **(2)** ! Tu veux _____ **(3)** quoi ?

– Un super _____ **(4)** !

– D'accord. Et l'_____ **(5)**, c'est pour moi !

– Mais non, je _____ **(6)** !

11 **Vous allez au restaurant. Écrivez l'ordre des actions.**

– manger et boire : ....

– payer : ....

– réserver : 1

– regarder la carte : ....

– choisir un plat ou un menu : ....

12 **Coline déjeune au restaurant. Soulignez le(s) mot(s) correct(s).**

– Bonjour madame, je vous apporte *la carte* / *la table* tout de suite.

– Ce n'est pas nécessaire. Je prends *le dessert* / *le menu* à 12 euros, s'il vous plaît.

– Bien, et vous prenez *une addition* / *une boisson* ?

– Non, de l'eau seulement. Je prendrai *un café* / *une entrée* après.

– Voici *le plat* / *le restaurant* d'aujourd'hui.

– Merci monsieur ! Je peux avoir *un menu* / *du sel*, s'il vous plaît ?

– Oui, bien sûr !

13 **Qui parle ? Le serveur ou le client ? Cochez.**

	serveur	client
Ex. : Vous prenez le menu spécial ?	✔	
1. Je peux avoir la carte ?		
2. Excusez-moi, je n'ai pas de fourchette.		
3. C'est pour déjeuner ?		
4. Vous prenez une entrée ?		
5. Non merci, pas de dessert.		
6. S'il vous plaît, je peux avoir un couteau ?		
7. Vous avez une table pour quatre ?		
8. L'addition, s'il vous plaît !		
9. Vous payez comment ?		

14 **Mettez les lettres dans l'ordre pour retrouver les 6 mots utilisés dans un restaurant.**

Ex. : e e d r s s t → le dessert

1. n a i d t o d i → l'..

2. s o b n i o s → une ....

3. r e e n t e → une ....

4. e r e v s r r e → ....

5. r a c e t → la ....

6. a l p t → un ....

BILAN

1 Vous préparez la table pour un dîner à la maison. Barrez l'intrus.

1. carte – fourchette – assiette

2. verre – addition – couteau

3. bouteille – petite cuillère – client

4. réserver – manger – mettre la table

5. fourchette – cuillère – menu

2 Mika téléphone au restaurant. Complétez.

dîner • table • réserver • déjeuner

– Allô, le restaurant Albert ?

– Oui.

– Je voudrais .... **(1)** une .... **(2)** pour demain, pour trois personnes.

– Oui, pour .... **(3)** ?

– Non, pour .... , **(4)** vers 20h.

– Très bien. Votre nom ?

3 Écoutez et complétez.

– Qu'est-ce qu'il y a dans le .... **(1)** à 18 euros ?

- Une .... **(2)**, un .... **(3)** et un .... **(4)**.

- C'est parfait.

- Et vous voulez une .... **(5)** ?

- Oui, je vais prendre une .... **(6)** d'................................ **(7)** gazeuse, s'il vous plaît.

- Très bien.

- Excusez-moi, j'ai une .... **(8)**, mais je n'ai pas de .... **(9)**.

- Je vous en apporte un tout de suite.

4 Complétez les phrases.

1. restaurant – menu – choisis → Au .... , je .... mon ....

2. prépares – repas → Tu .... le .... avant de mettre la table.

3. couteau – voulez – cuillère → Vous .... un .... ou une .... ?

4. petit déjeuner – boit – verre → Elle .... un grand .... d'eau avant son ....

5. paie – addition – demande → On .... l'................................ et on ....

6. dîner – dessert – prendre → Ils vont .... un bon .... à la fin du ....

Les commerces **13**

> Pour nommer les magasins
> Pour communiquer dans une situation d'achat

A Les magasins

 1 **Lisez et écoutez les mots.**

la boucherie	un magasin
la boulangerie	le marché
une boutique	la pâtisserie
le centre commercial	la pharmacie
la laverie	le supermarché

2 **Écrivez les mots.**

supermarché • boutique • marché • ~~magasin~~ • centre commercial

Ex. : un magasin

1. une b............................... de vêtements

2. un s...

3. un c........................... c...............................

4. un m...

3 **Mettez les lettres dans l'ordre pour retrouver les noms des magasins.**

Ex. : bchieeoru → une boucherie   **1.** aacehimpr → une ....   **2.** ierlvae → une ....

3. iersspitae → une ....   **4.** rieuoblaneg → une ....

4 **Retrouvez les noms des commerces.**

~~boucherie~~boutiquepâtisseriemarchémagasinpharmaciesupermarchélaverie

Ex. : une boucherie

1. une ....   **4.** un ....

2. une ....   **5.** une ....

3. un ....   **6.** un ....

                                  7. une ....

5 **Voici la liste de courses de Raphaël. Écrivez le nom des magasins où il doit aller.**

Ex. : Pour le pain, Raphaël va à la boulangerie.

1. Pour le rôti, il va à la ....

2. Pour les gâteaux, il va à la ....

3. Pour le dentifrice, il va à la ....

ou au ....

4. Pour les carottes et les tomates, il va

au .... ou au ....

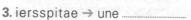

une baguette
① un rôti
② gâteaux
③ dentifrice
④ carottes et tomates

B Les achats

 6 **Lisez et écoutez les mots.**

L'argent	un (e) client(e)	acheter
un billet	un vendeur	coûter
une carte bancaire	une vendeuse	payer
les espèces		
l'euro		cher
le prix		

C'est combien ?
Ça coûte combien ?
Vous payez comment ?

7 **Écrivez les mots.**

argent • euro • espèces • carte bancaire • ~~billet~~ • prix

Ex.: un billet **1.** un e_ _ _ **2.** le p_ _ _ **3.** une c_ _ _ _ **4.** des e_ _ _ _ _ _

_ _ _ _ _ _ _ ou de l'a_ _ _ _ _

8 **Associez.**

1. Il achète.

2. Il coûte cher.

3. Il vend.

4. Son prix est en euros. **a.** le vendeur

5. Il donne le prix. **b.** le client

6. Il paye en espèces. **c.** le produit

7. Il n'est pas gratuit.

8. Il regarde le prix.

9. Il coûte 42 euros.

9 **Qui parle ? Le client ou le vendeur ? Cochez.**

	le client	le vendeur
Ex. : 84,50 euros, s'il vous plaît.		✔
1. Je peux payer par carte ?		
2. C'est quel prix ?		
3. Et pour vous, Monsieur ?		
4. Je voudrais…		
5. Je cherche…		
6. Vous désirez ?		
7. Désolé, nous n'acceptons pas les cartes bancaires.		

BILAN

1 **Écoutez et entourez le mot que vous entendez.**

1. laverie – boulangerie
2. pharmacie – pâtisserie
3. boulangerie – boucherie
4. marché – supermarché

5. argent – espèces
6. billet – payer
7. cliente – client
8. chèque – cher

2 **Pauline fait des courses dans 3 magasins. Complétez.**

euros • payer • prix • pharmacie • carte • cher • boutique de vêtements • combien • billet •
coûte • boulangerie

À la .... **(1)**

– Bonjour, je voudrais trois croissants, s'il vous plaît.

– Voilà.

– C'est .... **(2)** ?

– 4 euros.

– J'ai seulement un .... **(3)** de 20 euros.

– Ce n'est pas grave.

À la .... **(4)**

– Bonjour. Combien .... **(5)** ce dentifrice ?

– 5 .... **(6)**

– Oh, c'est .... **(7)** !

À la .... **(8)**

– 15 euros, c'est le .... **(9)** de ce tee-shirt ?

– Oui.

– Je vais .... **(10)** par .... **(11)**.

3 **Retrouvez les 10 mots cachés (la première lettre est en vert).**

L	P	R	I	X	M	H
A	A	E	W	Q	A	C
V	Y	U	C	U	R	L
E	E	R	H	Y	C	I
R	R	O	E	V	H	E
I	C	A	R	T	E	N
E	A	R	G	E	N	T
B	I	L	L	E	T	Z

Horizontalement →

1. le ....
2. une ....
3. l'...........................
4. un ....

Verticalement ↓

5. une ....
6. ....
7. un ....
8. ....
9. un ....
10. un ....

Les vêtements 14

> ❯ Pour nommer des vêtements et des accessoires
> ❯ Pour décrire des vêtements

A Les vêtements

 075

1 **Lisez et écoutez les mots.**

les bottes (fém.)	enlever
les chaussettes (fém.)	essayer
les chaussures (fém.)	mettre
une chemise	
un jean	
une jupe	
un manteau	
un pantalon	
un pull	
une robe	
un tee-shirt	
une veste	

> Je peux essayer ce manteau ?
> Mets tes chaussures !

2 **Regardez le dessin. Écrivez le début ou la fin des noms de vêtements.**

pull • robe • chemise • chaussures • manteau • ~~jean~~ • pantalon • jupe • chaussettes • veste • tee-shirt • bottes

Ex. : un jean

1. une _____te

2. une ju_____

3. un _____eau

4. des _____ures

5. un t_____-s_____

6. un pan_____

7. une _____se

8. une r_____

9. un _____l

10. des _____tes

11. des b_____

3 **Qui est qui ? Lisez les descriptions et écrivez le prénom de la personne.**

Ex. : Elahe a un manteau et une robe.

Carine a une veste, un pull, une jupe et des bottes.

Nathanaël a un tee-shirt, un jean et des chaussures de sport.

Kian a une veste, un pantalon et une chemise.

Ex. : Elahe   1. ....   2. ....   3. ....

4 **Mettez les lettres dans l'ordre pour retrouver le nom des vêtements.**

Ex. : e e s t v   → une veste

1. c e e h i m s   → une ....

2. a a e m n t u   → un ....

3. a e j n   → un ....

4. a c e e h s s s t t u   → des ....

5. a a l n n o p t   → un ....

6. l l p u   → un ....

076 **5** **Un parent aide ses enfants à préparer leurs valises. Écoutez et soulignez les phrases que vous entendez.**

Ex. : Arthur, prends deux pantalons. Arthur, prends cinq pulls.

1. N'oubliez pas vos chaussettes. N'oubliez pas vos chaussures.

2. Tu as ton jean ? Tu as ton manteau ?

3. Où sont vos tee-shirts ? Où sont vos chaussettes ?

4. Deux pantalons, Élodie, ça va ? Deux robes, Élodie, ça va ?

5. Et ta veste noire ? Et ta jupe noire ?

6. Quatre tee-shirts, c'est bien ! Quatre jeans, c'est bien !

7. Coralie, tu prends une jupe ? Coralie, tu prends une veste ?

6 **Complétez avec : *enlever, essayer, mettre*.**

Ex. : Elle veut essayer beaucoup de chaussures.

1. Il va m........................... son manteau.

2. Elle a chaud. Elle va e........................... sa veste.

3. Il va m................................ un jean et une chemise blanche.

4. Elle va e................................ deux jupes.

5. Il va en................................ son pantalon.

B Les accessoires

 7 **Lisez et écoutez les mots.**

> une ceinture
> un chapeau
> une écharpe
> des gants (masc.)
> des lunettes (de soleil) (fém.)
> un parapluie
> un sac à dos
> un sac à main

8 **Écrivez le nom des accessoires.**

écharpe • sac à main • ceinture • parapluie • ~~chapeau~~ • sac à dos • gants • lunettes de soleil

Ex.   1.   2.   3.   4.   5.   6.   7.

Ex. : un chapeau

1. une c................................

2. un p................................

3. un .... à m................

4. des l................ de s................

5. une é................................

6. un s................ à d................

7. des g................................

9 **Retrouvez le nom des accessoires. Ajoutez *un, une* ou *des*.**

~~écharpe~~parapluiegantsceinturechapeaulunettessac

Ex. : une écharpe

1. ....

2. ....

3. ....

4. ....

5. ....

6. ....

10 Regardez les dessins. Quels sont les accessoires qui ne sont pas sur le dessin b ?

a.

b.

Ex. : le chapeau

1. ....

2. ....

3. ....

4. ....

C Les couleurs et les matières

078 **11** Lisez et écoutez les mots.

Les couleurs		Les matières
blanc	orange	le coton
bleu	rose	le cuir
gris	rouge	la laine
jaune	vert	
noir		

12 Mettez les lettres dans l'ordre pour retrouver les couleurs.

Ex. : e g o r u :   **1.** b e l u   **2.** a e j n u   **3.** a b c l n   **4.** i n o r
rouge

5. e r t v ....   **6.** a e g n o r ....   **7.** g i r s ....   **8.** e o r s ....

13 Cochez *vrai* ou *faux*.

	vrai	faux
Ex. : bleu + jaune = vert	✔	
1. blanc + gris = gris		
2. rouge + bleu = rose		
3. blanc + noir = vert		
4. jaune + rouge = orange		
5. blanc + bleu = bleu		
6. noir + blanc = gris		

14 Remplissez la grille avec les couleurs.

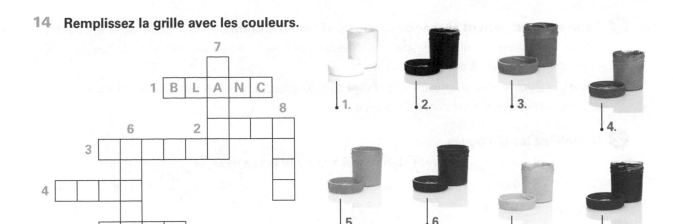

15 Complétez avec les noms des matières : *cuir, coton* ou *laine*.

Ex. : des chaussures en cuir   **1.** Un pull en l................... .   **2.** Un tee-shirt en c................... .

3. une écharpe en l................... .   **4.** Un sac en c................... .   **5.** Une chemise en c................... .

16 Selon la météo, quels vêtements ou quels accessoires prenez-vous ? Soulignez le mot correct.

Ex : Il fait froid. → une chemise en coton – <u>une écharpe</u>

1. Il fait chaud. → des gants en laine – un tee-shirt en coton

2. Il pleut. → un parapluie – un chapeau de soleil

3. Il fait beau. → un chapeau en laine – des lunettes de soleil

4. Il fait mauvais. → une chemise en coton – un parapluie

5. Il neige. → un manteau en laine – un tee-shirt en coton

6. Il fait froid. → une veste en coton – une veste en cuir

BILAN

(079) **1** **Anna et David partent en week-end. Quels vêtements prennent-ils ? Écoutez et entourez.**

Anna : une robe – un pull – une jupe – un tee-shirt – une veste – un manteau – des bottes – une écharpe – un sac à dos – un pantalon

David : une veste – un manteau – une chemise – des chaussures – un pantalon – un jean – des chaussettes – une ceinture – un parapluie

2 **Complétez les dialogues.**

sac • chaussures • cuir • bleues • essayer

Cliente : – Bonjour, je peux .... **(1)** ces .... **(2)** .... **(3)**, s'il vous plaît ?

Vendeuse : – Oui, voilà.

Cliente : – Elles sont très bien !

Vendeuse : – Avec, vous pouvez prendre ce beau .... **(4)** en .... **(5)**.

Cliente : – C'est une bonne idée. Merci, je vais réfléchir.

gants • verte • veste • noir • pantalon • mettre • robe • blancs

Marc : – Tu vas .... **(6)** quoi pour le mariage de Bertrand et Sonia ?

Alice : – Ma .... **(7)** .... **(8)** et j'ai des jolis .... **(9)**

.... **(10)** aussi. Et toi ?

Marc : – Un .... **(11)** .... **(12)** et une .... **(13)**.

3 **Soulignez le mot correct.**

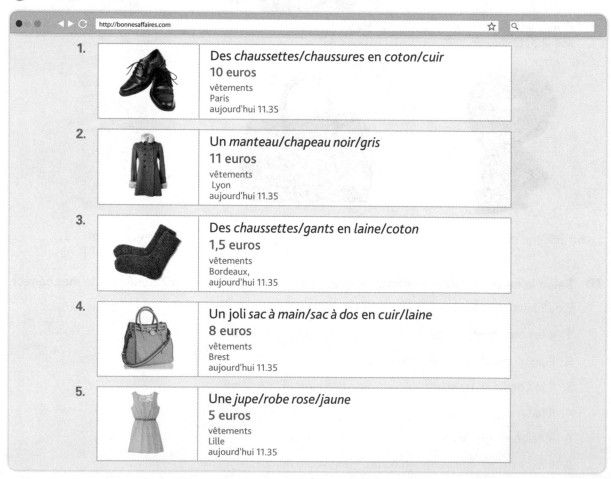

1. Des *chaussettes/chaussures* en *coton/cuir*
10 euros
vêtements
Paris
aujourd'hui 11.35

2. Un *manteau/chapeau noir/gris*
11 euros
vêtements
Lyon
aujourd'hui 11.35

3. Des *chaussettes/gants* en *laine/coton*
1,5 euros
vêtements
Bordeaux,
aujourd'hui 11.35

4. Un joli *sac à main/sac à dos* en *cuir/laine*
8 euros
vêtements
Brest
aujourd'hui 11.35

5. Une *jupe/robe rose/jaune*
5 euros
vêtements
Lille
aujourd'hui 11.35

La poste et la banque **15**

> Pour parler de la poste et de la banque
> Pour nommer les documents postaux et bancaires
> Pour décrire les actions à la poste et à la banque

A La poste

 1 **Lisez et écoutez les mots.**

l'adresse	**Le courrier**
la boîte aux lettres	la carte postale
le code postal	le colis
la poste	l'enveloppe
	la lettre
envoyer	le timbre
recevoir	

2 **Écrivez les mots.**

courrier • timbre • ~~poste~~ • colis • carte postale • boîte aux lettres • lettre • enveloppe

Ex : la poste

1. la b................................
aux l................................

2. le c................................

3. un c................................s

4. une l................................

5. une c................................ p................................

6. une e................................

7. un t................................

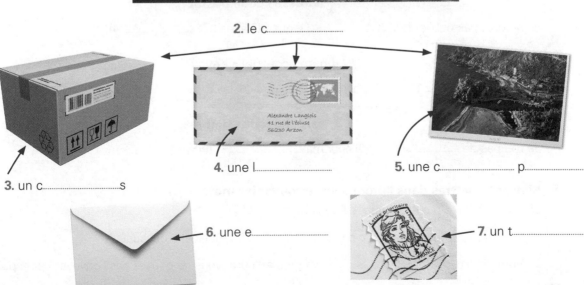

3 **Soulignez le mot correct.**

1. La dame va à *la poste* / *la boîte aux lettres* pour envoyer *une lettre* / *un colis*.

2. L'homme *envoie* / *reçoit* deux colis.

3. Il écrit *l'adresse* / *le timbre* sur une *enveloppe* / *carte postale*.

4 **Complétez.**

boîte aux lettres • enveloppe • ~~lettre~~

Je mets ma lettre d'abord dans une .... **(1)** puis dans la .... **(2)**.

adresse • code postal

Je ne dois pas oublier le .... **(3)** quand j'écris l'........................... **(4)**

poste • courrier • envoyer

Je vais à la .... **(5)** pour .... **(6)** le .... **(7)**

carte postale • timbre

Je n'ai pas de .... **(8)** pour ma .... **(9)**.

5 **Mettez les lettres dans l'ordre pour retrouver les mots.**

Ex. : Où est la (e o p s t) poste, s'il vous plaît ?

1. Tu préfères une (e e e l n o p p v) .... blanche ou jaune ?

2. Votre (c i l o s) .... est gros et lourd, vous ne pouvez pas l'envoyer par la poste.

3. Pour son anniversaire, on va lui (e e n o r v y) .... un petit cadeau.

4. C'est un (b e i m r t) .... très ancien ! Il est magnifique !

5. Je voudrais (c e e i o r r v) .... une (a c e r t) .... (a e l o p s t) ....

de tous les villages que vous allez visiter !

6. La (b e i o t) .... aux (e e l r s t t) .... est juste à côté du supermarché.

 6 **Léo est en vacances et veut écrire à son ami. Écoutez et complétez le dialogue.**

– Je vais envoyer une .... **(1)** à Brahim. Tu peux me donner son .... **(2)** ?

– 15 rue Beaubourg.

– Et le .... **(3)** ?

– 75003. Tu veux une .... **(4)** ?

– Oui, et tu as un .... **(5)** aussi ?

– Non, tu dois aller à la .... **(6)**.

– Le .... **(7)** part quand ?

– Cet après-midi ou demain.

B La banque

 7 **Lisez et écoutez les mots.**

l'argent	changer
le billet	retirer
la carte bancaire	
le chèque	
le compte	
le distributeur	
les espèces	

8 **Écrivez les mots.**

carte bancaire • espèces • changer • compte bancaire • distributeur • ~~argent~~ •
banque • retirer • chèque

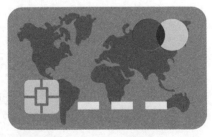

Ex.: l'argent

1. la b...

2. la c... b...

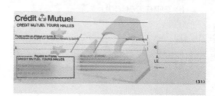

3. le ch_ _ _ _

4. le d_ _ _ _ _ _ _ _ _ _ _

5. les e_ _ _ _ _ _

6. le co_ _ _ _

7. c_ _ _ _ _ de l'argent

8. r_ _ _ _ _ de l'argent

9 **L'employé de la banque explique à Maria comment retirer de l'argent. Entourez le mot correct.**

Maria : – Excusez-moi, monsieur, je voudrais *retirer* / *payer* 150 *euros* / *espèces* **(1)**, s'il vous plaît.

L'employé : – Vous voulez *des espèces* / *un chèque* **(2)** ? Je suis désolé, on ne donne plus

d'argent / *de compte* **(3)** au guichet. Vous devez aller *au distributeur* / *chèque* **(4)**.

Maria : – Mais je n'ai pas l'habitude.

L'employé : – Vous avez *une carte bancaire* / *un distributeur* ? **(5)**

Maria : – Oui, bien sûr.

L'employé : – C'est très simple : vous mettez votre *argent* / *carte bancaire* **(6)** dans le *distributeur* / *compte* **(7)**. Vous suivez les instructions. C'est tout !

Maria : – Merci beaucoup.

L'employé : – N'oubliez pas votre carte et vos *comptes* / *billets* **(8)**.

Maria : – Au revoir monsieur.

10 **Écoutez et complétez.**

Ex : Vous allez à quelle banque ?

1. On va passer au _____ .

2. Tu as de l'_____ ?

3. Vous avez un _____ ici ?

4. J'ai un _____ de 200 euros.

5. On va _____ notre argent.

6. Nous ne pouvons pas accepter ce _____ .

7. Ils refusent les _____ .

8. Elle doit _____ 1500 euros.

11 **Associez.**

1. changer ou retirer •   • a. un chèque
2. signer •   • b. un code
3. taper •   • c. un compte
4. aller •   • d. le distributeur
5. utiliser •   • e. à la banque
6. payer •   • f. de l'argent
7. ouvrir •   • g. en espèces

12 **Lisez les phrases et remplissez la grille.**

1. J'écris et je signe mon …

2. On a besoin d'espèces, on va au …

3. Les … sont nécessaires pour payer quand on n'a pas de chèque et pas de carte bancaire.

4. Quand on a un … bancaire, on peut retirer de l'argent.

5. En France, le plus petit … est de 5 euros.

6. Si on veut des espèces, on peut aller à la banque pour …de l'argent.

7. Quand je veux des informations sur mon compte bancaire, je vais à la …

8. J'ai des euros et je veux des dollars, je dois … de l'argent.

9. Il est très difficile de vivre sans …

BILAN

1 Retrouvez les mots.

adresseargentespècescolistimbrecomptedistributeurchèquelettrebillet

1. l'...
2. l'...
3. des ....
4. le ....
5. le ....

6. le ....
7. le ....
8. le ....
9. la ....
10. le ....

084 **2** Écoutez. On est à la poste ou à la banque ? Cochez.

	1	2	3	4	5	6	7
à la poste							
à la banque							

3 Complétez les dialogues.

timbres • adresse • poste • colis • billet

À la .... **(1)**.

– Bonjour, je voudrais envoyer ce .... **(2)**.

– Oui, vous devez écrire l'..................... **(3)**, là.

– Voilà. Et je voudrais aussi des .... **(4)**.

  Je vous dois combien ?

– 8,50 euros.

– J'ai un .... **(5)** de 50 euros.

– Pas de problèmes.

changer • carte • distributeur • banque • espèces • retirer

À la .... **(6)**.

– Excusez-moi, monsieur, je dois .... **(7)**

  des .... **(8)**. Est-ce qu'il y a

  un .... **(9)** ici ?

– Oui, regardez, il est là. Vous avez votre .... **(10)**

  bancaire ?

– Oui, oui. Autre chose : je rentre des États-Unis.

  Je voudrais .... **(11)** des dollars.

– Oui. Combien ?

– 800. C'est possible ?

– Oui. Bien sûr.

Le téléphone et le numérique

❯ Pour décrire les téléphones et le numérique
❯ Pour parler de l'utilisation d'un téléphone et d'un ordinateur

A Le téléphone

1 Lisez et écoutez les mots.

une application	appeler
une carte SIM	envoyer
un chargeur	laisser
un écran	recharger
un message	répondre
un numéro de téléphone	téléphoner
un SMS	
un téléphone (portable)	
un smartphone	

> Allô, c'est la banque BSM ?
> Je t'appelle pour notre rendez-vous demain.

2 Écrivez les mots.

écran • **chargeur** • **numéro de téléphone** • **applications** • **carte SIM** • ~~smartphone~~ • **recharger**

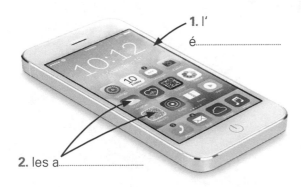

1. l'
é...

2. les a...

Ex. : un smartphone

3. un c... pour r... .

4. Une c... .

Rodolphe Petit

33 (0)6 53 84 18

5. Le n... de t... .

3 **Écrivez les mots.**

~~appelle~~ • numéro • recharger • application • répond • SMS • envoie • laisse • message

Ex. : Il appelle son ami.

1. Il cherche une a... .

2. Il e... un SMS.

3. Elle r... à une amie.

4. Il donne son n... .

5. Il l... un m... .

6. Je dois r... mon smartphone.

086 **4** **Écoutez et complétez le dialogue.**

– Je dois téléphoner à Rachid mais je n'ai pas mon .... **(1)**

–Tiens, voilà mon .... **(2)**.

– Je peux .... **(3)** un .... **(4)** ?

– Oui, bien sûr !

– Et il peut .... **(5)** un .... **(6)** ?

– Pas de problème, il connait mon .... **(7)** !

5 **Soulignez le mot qui convient.**

Ex : J'ai des *applications* / *chargeurs* sur mon écran.

1. L'identité de mon téléphone est sur ma carte *SIM* / *SMS*.

2. Je recharge mon portable avec *le numéro* / *le chargeur*.

3. Je lis mes messages sur *le numéro* / *l'écran* de mon téléphone.

4. J'appelle ma mère sur son *portable* / *SMS*.

B | Le numérique

087 **6** **Écoutez et lisez les mots.**

le clavier	allumer
une clé USB	cliquer
un courriel / un mél	enregistrer
un document	éteindre
Internet	poster (un commentaire)
le mot de passe	télécharger
un ordinateur (portable)	
les réseaux sociaux	
un site	
la souris	
une tablette	

7 **Écrivez les mots.**

tablette • souris • mél • site Internet • ~~ordinateur portable~~ • clavier • clé USB

Ex. : un ordinateur portable

1. une t...........................

2. une s...........................

3. une c...........................

4. un c...........................

5. un s...........................
l...........................

6. un m...........................

8 **Anna a beaucoup de matériel informatique. Complétez.**

clés usb • méls • ~~ordinateur portable~~ • sites • souris • tablettes

J'ai un ordinateur portable avec une s...........................**(1)**, deux t...........................**(2)** et

dix c...........................**(3)** ! Sur Internet, j'envoie des m...........................**(4)** à mes amis et je regarde

très souvent les s...........................**(5)** d'informations.

9 **Regardez Raphaël et écrivez ses actions.**

télécharge • clique • enregistre • ~~allume~~

Ex. : Raphaël allume son ordinateur

1. Il c.. sur un document.

2. Il t.. le document.

3. Il e.. le document.

10 **C'est le cours d'informatique. Soulignez le mot correct.**

« Vous *allumez* / *cliquez* votre ordinateur. Vous cherchez sur Internet *un site* / *une souris* **(1)**

d'informations, vous *cliquez* / *enregistrez* **(2)** sur le document avec la *souris* / *clé USB* **(3)**.

Vous *enregistrez* / *fermez* **(4)** le document sur votre *clé USB* / *mél* **(5)**. Pour finir, vous

ouvrez / *éteignez* **(6)** votre ordinateur. »

11 **Écrivez les mots.**

poste • réseaux sociaux • ~~mél~~ • commentaires • mot de passe

Ex. : J'envoie un mél.

1. Je vais souvent sur les r..

s..

2. Je p........................ des c........................ sur Facebook.

3. C'est un m........................ de p........................ très facile !

12 Associez.

1. s'informer •   • **a.** sur un document

2. allumer •   • **b.** une photo

3. enregistrer •   • **c.** sur Internet

4. cliquer •   • **d.** sur les réseaux sociaux

5. poster •   • **e.** un commentaire

6. aller •   • **f.** l'ordinateur

13 Barrez le mot incorrect.

Ex. : Je ne peux pas lire *ton mél* / *ta souris*.

1. J'envoie *un site* / *un mél*.

2. *J'enregistre* / *J'allume* l'ordinateur.

3. Je voudrais *un site* / *une tablette*.

4. Je vais acheter un autre *ordinateur portable* / *site*.

5. Je peux *télécharger* / *cliquer* ce film.

6. Je ne sais pas utiliser *ce clavier* / *ce mél*.

7. J'attends *son mél* / *son site*.

8. Je vais *poster* / *éteindre* un commentaire.

14 Écoutez et entourez les mots que vous entendez. (088)

clavier – éteindre – internet – souris – tablette – clé USB – mot de passe –

enregistrer – télécharger – site

1 **Lisez les phrases et remplissez la grille.**

1. Pour écrire sur mon ordinateur, j'ai besoin d'un …
2. Sur mon …, j'ai beaucoup d'applications.
3. Je lis des informations sur l'… de ma tablette.
4. Avec la …, je clique pour ouvrir un fichier.
5. J'envoie des … avec mon portable.
6. J'utilise un … pour recharger mon smartphone.
7. Si je ne connais pas le …, je ne peux pas téléphoner.

2 **Écoutez et complétez.**

1. Je vais .... mon ordinateur.
2. Il est vieux, ton .... !
3. On a oublié d'................................ les documents.
4. Je n'ai pas mon ....
5. Je vous envoie le .... demain.

6. Je ne veux pas .... trop vite.
7. Il faut .... votre ordinateur.
8. Regarde, j'ai un .... de Fabien.
9. Je vais lui .... un message.
10. On voudrait .... ce document.

3 **Retrouvez la publicité de la société Futuro.**

tablettes • ordinateurs • claviers • smartphones • Internet • clés USB

Venez aux journées spéciales de Futuro !

Pour l'informatique et le téléphone, nous sommes les leaders !

Nous avons des .... **(1)** et des .... **(2)**

pour aller sur .... **(3)** Et, bien sûr, des nouveaux .... **(4)** !

Mais chez nous, vous trouvez aussi : des .... **(5)**,

des .... **(6)**, tout le matériel que vous voulez ! Nous vous attendons.

La nature et le temps qu'il fait

❯ Pour décrire un lieu   ❯ Pour informer sur une saison

❯ Pour informer sur le temps qu'il fait

A La nature

090 **1** **Lisez et écoutez les mots.**

les arbres	la mer
la campagne	la montagne
le ciel	la nature
les fleurs	le paysage
la forêt	la rivière

2 **Écrivez les mots.**

arbre • campagne • ciel • fleurs • ~~paysages~~ • mer • montagne • rivière • forêt

Ex. : des paysages

1. une f.....................................

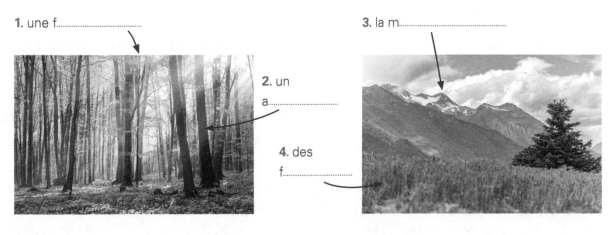

2. un
a.....................................

3. la m.....................................

4. des
f.....................................

5. le c.....................................

6. la c.....................................   **7.** une r.....................................   **8.** la m.....................................

3 **Mettez les lettres dans l'ordre pour retrouver les mots.**

Ex. : e i l c : le ciel

1. e m r : la ....

2. r f u e l s : les ....

3. u t n e r a : la ....

4. o t f r ê : la ....

5. v i è r r e i : la ....

6. b s r e r a : les ....

7. a a e g p s y : le ....

4 **Ces phrases sont-elles logiques ou pas ? Cochez.**

	logique	pas logique
Ex. : J'aime les arbres, je reste à la campagne.	✔	
1. Tu vas à la montagne parce que tu n'aimes pas la mer.		
2. Vous faites du ski, vous allez à la rivière.		
3. On déteste la nature, on habite dans une grande ville.		
4. Elle regarde le ciel parce qu'elle cherche une belle forêt.		
5. Nous voulons des fleurs, nous nous baignons dans la rivière.		
6. Ils se promènent dans la forêt parce qu'ils adorent les arbres.		

 5 **Chiara et Jörg parlent de leur logement en France. Écoutez et soulignez les mots corrects.**

1. Chiara : J'habite à la *campagne* / *mer*. De ma chambre, je vois une *rivière* / *forêt* avec

des *arbres* / *fleurs* magnifiques.

2. Jörg : Moi, je suis à la *campagne* / *montagne*, loin de la *rivière* / *mer*, mais dans la *nature* / *forêt*.

Il y a beaucoup de *fleurs* / *rivières* de toutes les couleurs en juin et juillet. Et *l'arbre* / *le ciel*

est toujours très beau !

B Le temps qu'il fait

6 **Lisez et écoutez les mots.**

les saisons	La météo
l'automne	il fait beau ≠ mauvais
l'été	il fait chaud ≠ froid
le printemps	il neige
l'hiver	il pleut
la neige	
les nuages	
la pluie	
le soleil	
le vent	

Il fait quel temps ?
Quel temps fait-il ?

7 **Écrivez les mots.**

printemps • ~~saisons~~ • hiver • automne • été

Ex. : En France, il y a quatre saisons.

1. Du 21/23 mars au 21/22 juin, c'est le p............................ .

2. Du 21/22 juin au 21/23 septembre, c'est l'é............................ .

3. Du 21/23 septembre au 21/22 décembre, c'est l'a............................ .

4. Du 21/22 décembre au 21/23 mars, c'est l'h............................ .

8 **Associez les mois et les saisons. (Plusieurs réponses sont possibles.)**

1. février •

2. avril •

3. juillet • • **a.** printemps

4. octobre • • **b.** été

5. novembre • • **c.** automne

6. août • • **d.** hiver

7. janvier •

8. mai •

9 **Mettez les lettres dans l'ordre pour retrouver les mots.**

Ex. : c e i l → le ciel

1. e i l l o s → le ....

2. a e g n u → un ....

3. e n t v → le ....

4. e e g i n → la ....

5. e i l p u → la ....

10 **Retrouvez les mots.**

venthivernuagesneigeprintempssoleilautomnepluieétésaisonmétéo

Ex. : le vent

1. l'............................   **6.** l'............................

2. les ....   **7.** la ....

3. la ....   **8.** l'............................

4. le ....   **9.** une ....

5. le ....   **10.** la ....

11 **Écrivez les mots.**

beau • chaud • neige • pleut • froid • ~~mauvais~~

Ex. : Il fait mauvais.

1. Il fait f.................................... .

2. Il n.................................... .

3. Il fait c.................................... .

4. Il fait b.................................... .

5. Il p.................................... .

12 **Soulignez la phrase correcte pour connaître le temps qu'il fait.**

Ex. : Il neige. → <u>Il fait froid.</u> / Il fait chaud.

1. Il fait mauvais. → Il y a beaucoup de vent. / Il y a beaucoup de soleil.

2. Il fait beau. → Il y a du soleil. / Il pleut.

3. C'est l'hiver. → Il fait chaud. / Il neige.

4. Il pleut. → Il fait beau. / Il y a des nuages.

5. C'est l'été. → Le vent est froid. / Le soleil est magnifique.

13 **Lisez les phrases et remplissez la grille.**

1. C'est de l'eau qui vient du ciel.

2. C'est la saison après l'hiver.

3. Elle est blanche, froide, mais très jolie !

4. Il est dans le ciel, rond, jaune et chaud.

5. C'est la saison après l'automne.

6. Ils sont blancs ou gris dans le ciel.

7. Il déplace les nuages.

8. C'est la saison après l'été.

1 P L U I E

14 **Écoutez et complétez les prévisions météo.**

« Bonjour à toutes et à tous ! Premier jour de l'été ! Quel .... **(1)** aujourd'hui ? Voici nos prévisions.

Attention aux .... **(2)** à Lyon. Il y a beaucoup de .... **(3)**, du .... **(4)** et .... **(5)**.

Une situation très différente à Lille : .... **(6)** et .... **(7)**, le .... **(8)** est magnifique ;

c'est sûr, l'.................... **(9)** est terminé dans le nord de la France ! »

BILAN

1 Classez les phrases dans le tableau.

Il y a des nuages. – Il y a une rivière. – C'est la mer. – Il y a du soleil. – Il y a des montagnes. – Il y a une grande forêt. – Il fait beau. – Il pleut. – Il fait froid. – Il fait mauvais. – La campagne est très verte. – Il neige. – Le paysage est très beau. – Il y a beaucoup de fleurs. – Les arbres sont magnifiques. – Il fait chaud.

pour décrire la nature	pour dire le temps qu'il fait
....	....
....	....
....	....
....	....
....	....
....	....
....	....

094 **2** Un ami vous conseille des chansons françaises sur le thème de la nature. Écoutez et complétez les titres.

1. Jean Ferrat : La .... (1965 – France)

2. Georges Brassens : Auprès de mon .... (1956 – France)

3. Édith Piaf : Sous le .... de Paris (1954 – France)

4. Charles Trenet : La .... (1946 – France)

5. Garou et Céline Dion : Sous le .... (2000 – Canada)

6. Bénabar : La .... (2015 – France)

7. Cali : Je rêve de voir l'.. (2012 – France)

8. Orelsan : La .... (2018 – France)

3 Soulignez le mot correct.

1. En *automne* / *hiver*, les *arbres* / *rivières* sont jaunes et rouges.

2. Aujourd'hui, il fait très *beau* / *mauvais* : il y a du soleil et pas de *nuages* / *fleurs*.

3. Le *printemps* / *soleil* est ma saison préférée : j'aime voir les *arbres* / *nuages* devenir verts et les *fleurs* / *soleils* partout dans la *campagne* / *mer*.

4. Près de chez moi, il y a une grande *forêt* / *mer* avec de très beaux *nuages* / *arbres*.

5. Quand il fait *mauvais* / *beau*, je me promène dans la *campagne* / *rivière*.

6. Le *ciel* / *printemps* est magnifique avec ces *vents* / *nuages*.

7. J'adore les *paysages* / *étés* de *vent* / *fleurs*.

18 Le voyage et les vacances

> Pour parler des transports en voyage
> Pour parler d'un voyage
> Pour nommer les logements de vacances

A Le voyage

 1 **Lisez et écoutez les mots.**

l'aéroport	le sac
l'aller ≠ le retour	le train
l'aller-retour	la valise
l'arrivée ≠ le départ	le vol
l'avion	
le bagage	arriver ≠ partir
le bateau	réserver / faire une réservation
le billet	
le car	
la gare	

> Je voudrais un billet pour Rome, un aller-retour.

2 **Écrivez les mots.**

car • gare • train • sac • valise • avion • ~~aéroport~~ • bagages

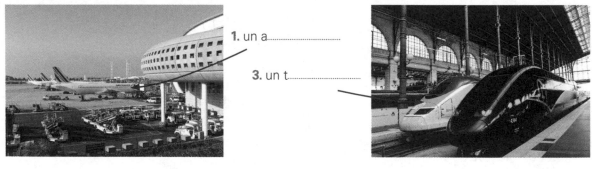

1. un a.............................

3. un t.............................

Ex. : un aéroport

2. une g.............................

5. les b.............................

6. un s.............................

4. un c.............................

7. une v.............................

3 **Barrez l'intrus.**

Ex. : ~~gare~~ – avion – vol

1. bateau – bagages – car

2. aéroport – bateau – avion

3. sac – avion – valise

4. gare – train – car

5. bagages – valise – bateau

4 **Complétez.**

part • départ • arrive • ~~billet~~ • arrivée • retour • aller

Ex. : C'est un billet de train

1. L'a _ _ _ _ est le 11 juillet.

2. Le train p _ _ _ de Paris.

3. Le d _ _ _ _ _ est à 19h26.

4. Le train a _ _ _ _ _ à Tours à 20h47.

5. Le r _ _ _ _ _ est le 14 juillet.

6. Le 14 juillet, l'a _ _ _ _ _ _ à Paris est à 19h31.

5 **Sarah et Dylan parlent de leur voyage. Écoutez et complétez le dialogue.**

Sarah : – Tu dois réserver ton .... **(1)** pour le retour ?

Dylan : – Non, j'ai acheté un .... **(2)**.

Sarah : – Super ! Le .... **(3)** du .... **(4)** est à 7h15.

Dylan : – On se donne rendez-vous à la .... **(5)** ?

Sarah : – Oui, d'accord. Je prends un .... **(6)**, pas de .... **(7)**. Et toi ?

Sarah : – Je ne sais pas encore, mais un petit .... **(8)**, c'est sûr.

6 **Barrez la phrase qui n'a pas de sens.**

Ex. : On réserve un billet. ~~On réserve un aéroport.~~

1. Vous attendez le train. Vous attendez la gare.

2. Nous ne réservons pas l'information. Nous n'avons pas l'information.

3. Le départ est complet. L'avion est à 8h00.

4. Monsieur, c'est votre bagage ? Monsieur, c'est votre aller ?

5. L'aller-retour est à 6h37. Le départ est à 6h37.

6. Je voudrais un aller pour Nice. Je voudrais une arrivée pour Nice.

7. Écoute, ils annoncent le départ. Écoute, ils annoncent le billet.

8. Tu connais l'heure d'arrivée de l'aéroport ? Tu connais l'heure d'arrivée du vol ?

7 **Complétez les dialogues.**

~~aéroport~~ • avion • billet • complet • réserver • vol

À l'aéroport :

– Bonjour madame. Je cherche un .... **(1)** pour Vienne.

– L'............................... **(2)** de 15h15 est .... **(3)**. Vous pouvez .... **(4)** pour 17h00,

vous voulez un .... **(5)** ?

– Oui merci.

arrivée • gare • sac • train • valise

À la .... : **(6)**

– Tu peux attendre avec moi l'............................... **(7)** du .... **(8)** de Marion ?

– Oui, bien sûr, elle va avoir un .... **(9)** et une grosse .... **(10)**, comme d'habitude.

B Les lieux et les logements de vacances

 8 **Lisez et écoutez les mots.**

le camping
la chambre
la clé
complet
l'hôtel
une location
la réception
la tente
aller (à la campagne, à la mer, à la montagne)
louer

> Je suis désolé, l'hôtel est complet.

9 **Complétez.**

clé • tente • ~~réception~~ • hôtel • chambre • location • camping

Ex. : La réception de l'h............................... **(1)**

Voici la c............................... **(2)**,

c'est la ch............................... **(3)** numéro 10.

Alex fait du c............................... **(4)** ;

Il a une t............................... **(5)** rouge.

La famille Bizet va passer ses vacances

dans une l............................... **(6)**

10 **Associez.**

1. Je cherche le calme.
2. Je fais du camping.
3. Je n'ai pas la clé.
4. J'adore l'eau.
5. Je déteste la neige.
6. Je suis en vacances avec des amis.
7. Je veux me reposer et je ne veux rien faire.

a. J'ai trouvé une grande location.
b. J'ai une tente.
c. Je demande à la réception.
d. Je ne vais pas à la montagne.
e. Je vais à l'hôtel.
f. Je suis à la campagne.
g. Je vais à la mer.

098 **11** **Écoutez et complétez.**

Ex : L'hôtel est très calme.

1. On a une grande ....

2. Je prends ma .... à la ....

3. Il fait froid sous la ....

4. Comment est votre .... ?

5. Nous sommes dans un .... près de la mer.

12 **Madame Leblanc et Madame Lenoir parlent de vacances. Complétez le dialogue.**

loué • camping • hôtel • tente • réserver • ~~vacances~~ • chambre

– Pour les prochaines vacances, on va à New York. On a .... **(1)** un appartement. Et vous ?

– Nous, on préfère .... **(2)** une belle .... **(3)** dans un petit .... **(4)** à la montagne.

– Et le .... **(5)**, vous n'aimez pas ?

– Si, mais notre .... **(6)** est très vieille et pas facile à transporter.

– Nous allons avoir des souvenirs de vacances très différents !

13 **Lisez les phrases et remplissez la grille.**

1. Quand on aime la neige, on va à la … en hiver.

2. On fait du … parce qu'on veut dormir dans la nature.

3. On cherche une … pour 8 personnes pour les vacances.

4. On demande la … de la chambre.

5. On ne va pas à l' … , c'est trop cher !

6. Quand on arrive l'hôtel, on va à la … .

7. On part au camping avec une … .

BILAN

(099) **1** Écoutez et associez les phrases aux dessins. Cochez.

	1	2	3	4	5	6	7	8	9	10

2 Qui parle ? L'employé ou le client ? Associez.

1. Voici votre clé. •
2. Je voudrais un billet pour Nantes. •
3. Où voulez-vous aller ? •
4. Je voudrais faire une réservation. • • **a.** le client
5. Vous voulez un aller-retour ? • • **b.** l'employé
6. Le vol est complet, je suis désolé. •
7. Vous avez des bagages ? •
8. Voici votre billet. •

3 Noémie et François parlent de leurs prochaines vacances. Complétez.

billet • **camping** • **pars** • **loue** • **retour** • **avion** • **hôtel**

– Tu fais quoi, François, cet été ?

– Je reste en France. Je vais faire du .... **(1)** dans les Alpes avec ma famille.

Et toi Noémie, tu .... **(2)** où ?

– Je vais au Maroc. Je prends l'............................... **(3)** le 23 juillet et j'ai mon .... **(4)**

de .... **(5)** le 7 août.

– Et tu vas à l'............................... **(6)** ?

– Non, je .... **(7)** une maison avec des amis.

– Super ! Tu m'envoies des photos, d'accord ?

19 L'école et les études

❯ Pour nommer le matériel pour étudier
❯ Pour parler des lieux d'études
❯ Pour parler d'apprentissage

A Le matériel pour étudier

 1 Lisez et écoutez les mots.

un classeur	un ordinateur
un crayon	une page
un dictionnaire	du papier
une feuille	un stylo
un livre	une tablette

2 Écrivez les mots.

crayon • tablette • dictionnaire • ~~classeur~~ • page • ordinateur • papier • feuille • livre • stylo

3. une p...................

Ex. : un classeur   **1.** une f...................   **2.** un l...................   **4.** un c...................   **5.** un s...................

6. un d...................   **7.** du p...................   **8.** un o...................   **9.** une t...................

3 Complétez.

~~pages~~ • feuilles • dictionnaire • papier • crayon • tablette

Ex. : Mon livre a 150 pages.

1. Je mets les .... dans mon classeur.

2. J'allume ma ....

3. Mon .... est lourd.

4. Pour écrire, tu veux un .... ou un stylo ?

5. Je voudrais du .... pour dessiner.

4 **Écoutez et cochez les objets que Baptiste a dans son sac.**

	dans son sac	pas dans son sac
1. une tablette	✔	
2. un dictionnaire		
3. un livre		
4. un ordinateur		
5. du papier		
6. un stylo		
7. un classeur		

5 **Classez les mots dans le tableau. (Plusieurs réponses sont possibles.)**

~~un stylo~~ • un dictionnaire • une tablette • du papier • un classeur • un crayon • une feuille • un ordinateur • une page

pour écrire	pour lire
un stylo, ...	....
....	....
....	....
....	....

B | Les lieux

 6 **Lisez et écoutez les mots.**

la bibliothèque	un lycée
la cafétéria	une salle (de cours)
un collège	le secrétariat
une école	une université

7 **Écrivez les mots.**

lycée • université • ~~école~~ • collège

Ex. : Il va à l'école. **1.** Elle va au c.............................. . **2.** Il va au l.............................. . **3.** Elle va à l'u.............................. .

8 Soulignez la réponse correcte.

Ex. : Jeanne a 22 ans, elle va *au collège* / *à l'université*.

1. Ali a 6 ans, il va à *l'école* / *au lycée*.

2. Karim et Thomas ont 13 ans, ils vont *au collège* / *à l'école*.

3. Lisa a 17 ans, elle va *à l'école* / *au lycée*.

9 Écrivez les mots sur le dessin.

salles de cours • bibliothèque • cafétéria • ~~Université~~ • secrétariat

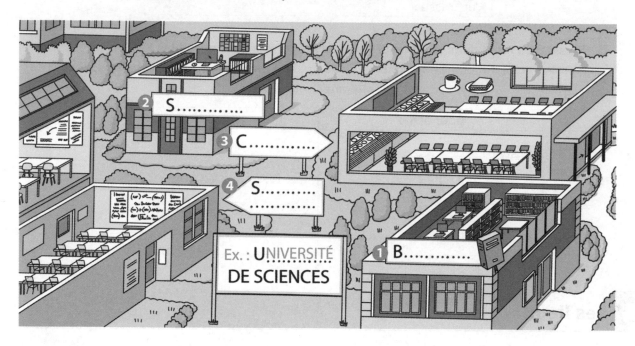

10 Associez.

1. Adèle étudie   •   • **a.** à la bibliothèque

2. Elle choisit des livres   •   • **b.** à l'université

3. Elle va déjeuner   •   • **c.** au secrétariat

4. Elle demande des informations •   • **d.** dans la salle de cours

5. Elle écoute   •   • **e.** à la cafétéria

103 **11 Écoutez et soulignez le mot que vous entendez.**

Ex. : Chez moi, il y a trois *collèges* / *écoles*.

1. C'est *un lycée* / *une université* moderne.

2. La *cafétéria* / *bibliothèque* est à côté du secrétariat.

3. Cette *salle de cours* / *école* est fermée aujourd'hui.

4. *Le secrétariat* / *La cafétéria* est au premier étage.

5. J'ai adoré *mon lycée* / *mon université*.

6. Où est *l'école* / *l'université*, s'il vous plaît ?

C L'apprentissage

(104) 12 Lisez et écoutez les mots.

un cours	apprendre	préparer un examen
un(e) élève	étudier	passer un examen
un(e) étudiant(e)	expliquer	réussir un examen
un examen		difficile ≠ facile
un(e) professeur(e)		

13 Écrivez les mots.

apprendre • explique • professeur • élèves • ~~cours~~ • étudie • étudiante • prépare • examen

C'est un cours : les é.................................. **(1)**

doivent a.................................. **(2)** le français,

le p.................................. **(3)** e.................................. **(4)**.

Elle est é.................................. **(5)**. Elle é.................................. **(6)**

à la bibliothèque. Elle p.................................. **(7)**

un e.................................. **(8)**.

14 Entourez le mot qui convient.

Ex. : (L'étudiant) / Le cours a un examen.

1. Le professeur explique *le cours* / *l'étudiant*.

2. *Les élèves* / *les examens* étudient.

3. Le professeur explique à *l'étudiant* / *l'examen*.

4. *Les cours* / *Les élèves* apprennent.

5. Le cours est *difficile* / *facile* : je comprends bien.

6. Paul étudie : il va *passer* / *réussir* un examen le mois prochain.

(105) 15 Écoutez et complétez le dialogue.

– Vous êtes étudiante ?

– Oui, et je .... **(1)** mon dernier .... **(2)** demain !

– Bon ! Vous allez .... **(3)**.

– J'espère ! Si je .... **(4)**, je vais être .... **(5)**, je vais donner des .... **(6)** !

– Alors, bonne chance !

BILAN

1 Eugène propose cette petite annonce. Complétez.

élèves • cours • Étudiant • lycée • examens

.... (1) donne des .... (2) de français
à des .... (3) de .... (4) pour préparer
les .... (5).
Contacter Eugène@bv.net

2 Écoutez et complétez.

1. On va à la ....

2. Tu as ton .... ?

3. Elle va .... un .... la semaine prochaine.

4. Mon .... est près de la maison.

5. J'ai oublié mon ....

6. Cet exercice n'est pas ....

3 Lisez les phrases et remplissez la grille.

1. J'écris avec un … .

2. Brice a 18 ans, il étudie au … .

3. Coralie a 23 ans, elle étudie à l' … .

4. Ce livre à 450 … .

5. Le … explique aux étudiants.

6. Les … écoutent le professeur.

7. Lundi, j'ai 5 heures de … .

8. Demain, je passe un … .

4 Qui parle ? Le professeur ou l'étudiant ? Cochez.

	le professeur	l'étudiant
1. Je vais étudier à la bibliothèque.		
2. On passe l'examen mardi.		
3. Regardez page 56.		
4. Tu vas à la cafétéria ?		
5. Vous avez une question ?		
6. Ce n'est pas facile !		
7. Je dois réussir !		
8. Attendez, je vais expliquer.		
9. Tu as un stylo ?		
10. Prenez votre livre.		

Le travail **20**

> Pour nommer les professions

> Pour parler de son travail

> Pour parler de l'entreprise

A Les professions

 1 Lisez et écoutez les mots.

un acteur / une actrice	un / une journaliste
un agriculteur / une agricultrice	un médecin
un(e) avocat(e)	un / une photographe
un(e) chauffeur(e)	un policier / une policière
un(e) commerçant(e)	un pompier / une pompière
un(e) garagiste	
un(e) ingénieur(e)	travailler (à l'intérieur / à l'extérieur)

2 Écrivez les mots.

agriculteur • ingénieur • actrice • ~~avocate~~ • policière • photographe • journaliste • garagiste • médecin • chauffeur • commerçant • pompier

Ex. : une avocate

1. un i...............................

2. une j...........................

3. un m...........................

4. un a............................

5. un c.................. de taxi

6. une p...........................

7. un p............................

8. une a...........................

9. un c............................

10. un g...........................

11. un p...........................

3 **Retrouvez les professions.**

~~commerçant~~acteuravocatmédecinagricultricepolicieringénieurechauffeur

Ex. : un commerçant

1. un ....

2. un ....

3. un ....

4. une ....

5. un ....

6. une ....

7. un ....

4 **Associez chaque phrase à 2 professions.**

1. Il travaille généralement à l'extérieur. •

2. Il travaille généralement à l'intérieur. •

3. Il a une profession artistique. •

4. Il travaille dans la sécurité. •

- **a.** l'avocat
- **b.** l'agriculteur
- **c.** le chauffeur
- **d.** le médecin
- **e.** le photographe
- **f.** l'acteur
- **g.** le pompier
- **h.** le policier

108 **5** **Écoutez et complétez le dialogue.**

– Élise, tu veux faire quoi, plus tard ?

– Moi, je voudrais être .... **(1)** ou .... **(2)**. C'est très différent, je sais. Et toi, Amir ?

– Moi, je veux être à l'extérieur. .... **(3)**, j'aimerais bien. Mais ce n'est pas facile.

Alors, ... **(4)**, pourquoi pas ?

– Ce n'est pas du tout la même chose ! Moi, je serai .... **(5)** ! C'est sûr !

– Moi, j'adore conduire ! Je serai .... **(6)** et, si ce n'est pas possible, ... **(7)**

– Ou alors, comme mon père, ... **(8)**

– Rendez-vous dans 10 ans !

B L'entreprise

109 **6** **Lisez et écoutez les mots.**

un(e) assistant(e)	chercher un travail
un(e) collègue	suivre une formation
un directeur / une directrice	être au chômage
un(e) employé(e)	
un bureau	
le chômage	

Vous travaillez où ?

7 **Écrivez les mots.**

bureau • directeur • ~~collègues~~ • employé • assistant

Ex. : les collègues

DIRECTION

1. le b........................... **2.** le d........................... **3.** l'a........................... **4.** l'e...........................

8 *Vrai* ou *faux* ? **Cochez.**

	vrai	faux
Ex. : Je ne travaille pas, je suis au chômage.	✔	
1. Il n'a pas de profession, il a un travail.		
2. Ils sont au chômage, ils travaillent dans une entreprise.		
3. Tu suis une formation, tu apprends.		
4. Ils cherchent un travail, ils sont au chômage.		
5. On n'a pas d'emploi. On est au chômage.		

Pas de travail
=
le chômage

Suivre une formation
=
apprendre

110 **9** **Écoutez et complétez.**

Ex. : Je voudrais trouver un travail rapidement.

1. Elle est ...., elle veut devenir ....

2. Vous êtes au .... ? Vous pouvez .... une ....

3. On .... un travail dans une .... française.

10 **Complétez pour connaître les professions de la famille Dupont.**

formation • directeur • entreprise • au chômage • assistante • ~~travail~~ • suivre

Madame Dupont a trouvé un travail dans l'........................ **(1)** Bardeau : elle est .... **(2)**

du .... **(3)** ; son mari ne travaille pas, il est .... **(4)**. Leur fille a un projet :

elle va .... **(5)** une .... **(6)** pour être ingénieure.

BILAN

1 Une entreprise cherche un employé. Barrez le mot incorrect.

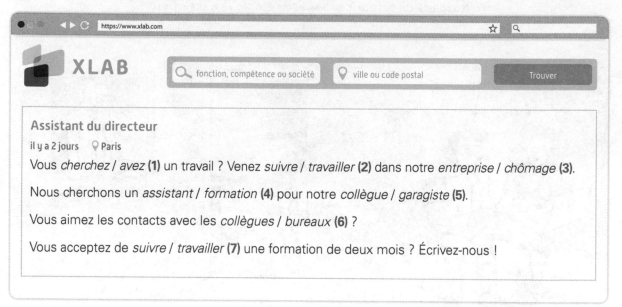

> **XLAB**
>
> 🔍 fonction, compétence ou société   📍 ville ou code postal   Trouver
>
> **Assistant du directeur**
>
> il y a 2 jours   📍 Paris
>
> Vous *cherchez* / *avez* **(1)** un travail ? Venez *suivre* / *travailler* **(2)** dans notre *entreprise* / *chômage* **(3)**.
>
> Nous cherchons un *assistant* / *formation* **(4)** pour notre *collègue* / *garagiste* **(5)**.
>
> Vous aimez les contacts avec les *collègues* / *bureaux* **(6)** ?
>
> Vous acceptez de *suivre* / *travailler* **(7)** une formation de deux mois ? Écrivez-nous !

🎧 111 **2** Écoutez et complétez.

1. Amélie travaille dans un ....

2. Gaëlle a un bon ....

3. Karine est ....

4. Kadder est ....

5. Tiago est .... chez un ....

6. Sonia est ....

7. Janeck .... dans l' .... XLAB.

3 Lisez les phrases et remplissez la grille.

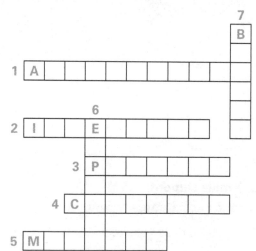

1. Il travaille à la campagne.

2. Il travaille beaucoup avec les techniques.

3. Il porte un uniforme et travaille dans la sécurité.

4. Je travaille avec Kader ; c'est mon …

5. On va le voir quand on est malade.

6. Il travaille dans une entreprise.

7. C'est la pièce où travaille le directeur.

CHAPITRE

1 L'identité

A L'état civil

2 1. un permis de conduire 2. une carte d'étudiant 3. une fiche d'inscription 4. un passeport 5. une carte d'identité

4 1. la nationalité 2. le nom 3. le prénom 4. la date de naissance 5. le sexe 6. l'adresse

5 1. homme 2. féminin, femme

6 2. a 3. f 4. d 5. e 6. c

7 (004) **Ex. :** C'est monsieur Charif.

1. américain	5. Madrid
2. Mon prénom ? Paul.	6. Je m'appelle Max.
3. C'est un homme.	7. Vous êtes français ?
4. Elle est japonaise.	8. Madame Fortin.

Nom : 8 **Prénom :** 2, 6 **Nationalité :** 1, 4, 7 **Lieu de naissance :** 5 **Sexe :** 1, 2, 3, 4, 5, 7, 8

8 1. g 2. c, d, f 3. a, e, h

B L'adresse

10 1. l'adresse 2. le numéro 3. la ville 4. le code postal 5. le pays

11 1. Michèle 2. France 3. 6, avenue de l'Est Nancy 4. 56 5. Strasbourg 6. rue Victor Hugo 7. LAMARQUE

12 1. h 2. c, e 3. b, f 4. a, g

C L'âge

14 2. c 3. b 4. a 5. f 6. e 7. j 8. h 9. k 10. l 11. i 12. g

15 1. août 2. décembre 3. février 4. janvier 5. juillet 6. juin 7. mai 8. mars 9. novembre 10. octobre 11. septembre

16 2. juillet 3. mai 4. novembre 5. décembre 6. octobre 7. juin 8. janvier 9. avril 10. août 11. septembre 12. février

17 (007) **Ex. :** On est en septembre.

1. Il a 20 ans.	5. Vous avez quel âge ?
2. Tu es né en 2005.	6. C'est la date exacte ?
3. Le 20 juin 2019.	7. Il est né en 2010.
4. Mon grand-père a 95 ans !	8. Je suis né en avril.

année de naissance : 2, 3, 7 **âge :** 1, 4, 5 **date :** 3, 6 **mois :** 3, 8

BILAN

1 1. le nom 2. la nationalité 3. l'adresse 4. le sexe 5. la date de naissance 6. l'âge 7. le prénom 8. le lieu de naissance 9. le mois

2 (008) 1. Quelle est votre nationalité ?
2. Quel est votre prénom ?
3. Vous vous appelez comment ?
4. Quel est votre nom de famille ?
5. Quel est votre lieu de naissance ?
6. Quelle est votre adresse ?
7. Vous habitez à quel numéro ?

1. e 2. g 3. b 4. c 5. a 6. f 7. d

3 **Nom :** DUVALIER **Prénom :** Eliot **Sexe :** masculin **Nationalité :** canadienne **Date de naissance :** 28 décembre 2002 **Ville de naissance :** Montréal **Adresse :** 130, rue d'Alésia **Code postal :** 75014 **Ville :** Paris

CHAPITRE

2 Les moments de la journée, l'heure et les jours de la semaine

A Les moments de la journée

2 1. nuit 2. journée 3. matin 4. après-midi 5. soir 6. nuit

3 1. l'après-midi 2. la nuit 3. le soir 4. la nuit 5. la matin 6. l'après-midi

B L'heure

5 1. horaires 2. heures / minutes / secondes 3. heure

6 1. horaires 2. l'heure 3. secondes 4. minutes

8 2. g 3. f 4. e 5. h 6. a 7. c 8. d

9 1. 12h00 2. 19h00 3. 8h30 4. 11h15 5. 23h30 6. 13h00

10 (012) **Ex. :** Il est 9 heures moins le quart du matin. Il est 8h45

1. Il est midi.
2. Il est 2 heures de l'après-midi.
3. Il est 11 heures du soir.
4. Il est minuit.
5. Il est 4 heures moins le quart de l'après-midi.
6. Il est 7 heures et demie du matin.

1. 12h00 2. 14h00 3. 23h00 4. 0h00 5. 15h45 6. 7h30 7. 22h15

11 4 en avance 2, 6 à l'heure 1, 3, 5 en retard

12 3, 6 : a 2, 4, 5, 7, 8 : b

C Les jours de la semaine

14 1. samedi : 6 2. jeudi : 4 3. mardi : 2 4. dimanche : 7 5. mercredi : 3 6. vendredi : 5

15 1. dimanche 2. mercredi 3. mardi 4. lundi 5. samedi 6. vendredi

16 1. week-end 2. Aujourd'hui / Demain / Hier

17 **vrai :** 2, 3, 5, 6 **faux :** 1, 4

18 (014) 1. Ma sœur arrive **demain** (1). 2. Le magasin est fermé le **dimanche** (2). 3. Ce **week-end** (3), nous partons à la campagne. 4. Le **lundi** (4) et le **jeudi** (5), je vais à la piscine. 5. Vous venez **samedi** (6) ? Très bien. 6. Elle part à Berlin pendant une **semaine** (7).

BILAN

1 1. horaires 2. minute 3. semaine 4. jeudi 5. matin 6. heure 7. minuit 8. mercredi

2 (015) – Bonjour monsieur je téléphone pour un **rendez-vous** (1) avec le docteur Delorme.
– Oui, pour quand ?
– **Aujourd'hui** (2), c'est possible ?
– Ce **matin** (3), le docteur n'est pas là. Mais cet **après-midi** (4), c'est possible.
– À quelle **heure** (5) ?
– À 15 **heures** (6), ça va ?
– Oui, très bien
– Vous êtes madame ?
– Madame Mourier.
– Bien merci. A tout à l'heure, madame Mourier.

3 1. horaires 2. matin 3. heures 4. après-midi 5. soir 6. samedi

3 La famille

A La situation de famille

2 1. couple 2. marié 3. célibataire 4. copain 5. femme
6. divorcé 7. veuve

3 2. c 3. a 4. d 5. f 6. e

4 (017) 1. Voici mon mari, Antoine. 2. Elle est divorcée ?
3. Tu es la copine de Thomas ? 4. Vous êtes un couple
jeune ! 5. Lucie, c'est ta femme ? 6. Elle va vivre avec
Akim. 7. Monsieur Alliot, vous êtes célibataire ?

B Les membres de la famille

6 1. le père 2. la mère 3. le fils 4. la fille 5. les enfants

7 une femme : 1. la fille 2. la grand-mère 3. la sœur
un homme : 4. le frère 5. le père 6. le fils 7. le grand-père

8 2. a 3. d 4. e 5. c

9 1. frère 2. père 3. parents 4. sœur 5. grand-père,
grand-mère 6. fils 7. mère 8. enfants

10 (019) Ex. : Jules est le fils d'Inès.
1. Dany est la sœur de Jérôme.
2. Vincent est le mari d'Inès.
3. Izïa est la femme de Kader.
4. Inès est la grand-mère de Dany et Jules.
5. Martine est la fille de Vincent.

2, 3, 4 vrai **1, 5, 6** faux

BILAN

1 1. couple 2. célibataire 3. veuve 4. marié 5. copine
6. sœur 7. divorcés

2 1. veuf 2. copain 3. marié 4. célibataire 5. copine
6. vivre seul 7. fils

3 (020) 1. Isabelle est ma femme.
2. On est pacsés.   5. Mes parents sont séparés.
3. Maylis est ma petite fille. 6. Mon fils est célibataire.
4. Jordan est mon frère.   7. Ilian et Éloïse sont mariés.
1. a - 2. a - 3. b – 4. a – 5. b – 6. a – 7. b

4 La vie quotidienne

A Les activités quotidiennes

2 1. Il se lève. 2. Elle prend son petit-déjeuner. 3. Elle
se couche. 4. Il dort. 5. Ils travaillent.

3 2. Il se lève. 3. Il prend son petit déjeuner. 4. Il travaille.
5. Il dîne. 6. Il se couche. 7. Il dort.

4 1. Il fait le ménage. 2. Ils dinent. 3. Elles déjeunent.
4. Il fait la cuisine.

5 (022) 1. Je me lève à 8 heures et demie.
2. Line prend son petit déjeuner à 7h et quart.
3. On se couche à 23 heures.

4. Gaël se réveille à 7 heures.
5. Alice fait les courses à 11 heures.
6. Nous dînons à 20h30.
7. Jean dort à minuit.
8. Paul fait la cuisine à midi.
9. Il fait le ménage à 9 heures.
10. Tu déjeunes à 13h.

2. b **3.** j **4.** i **5.** a **6.** e **7.** g **8.** h **9.** f **10.** d

B L'hygiène

7 1. savon 2. dentifrice 3. rasoir 4. brosse à dents
5. shampoing

8 1. prend une douche 2. coiffe 3. brosse les dents 4. rase

9 1. frère 2. père 3. parents 4. sœur 5. grand-père,
grand-mère 6. fils 7. mère 8. enfants

10 1. shampoing 2. dentifrice 3. savon 4. douche 5. serviette

11 1. shampoing 2. serviette 3. dentifrice 4. douche
5. savon 6. rasoir

BILAN

1 1. faire les courses 2. se laver les mains 3. faire la
cuisine 4. déjeuner
1. se réveiller 2. se lever 3. prendre son petit déjeuner
4. se brosser les dents
1. travailler 2. dîner 3. se coucher 4. dormir

2 (024) 1. se lever 2. faire la cuisine 3. se coucher
4. se doucher 5. se réveiller 6. se raser

3 1. fais les courses 2. déjeune 3. travailles
4. dentifrice 5. me douche

5 Les loisirs

A Les activités sportives

2 1. vélo 2. running 3. tennis 4. marche 5. natation
6. équitation 7. basket 8. gymnastique

3 (026) 1. natation 2. tennis 3. football 4. running 5. vélo
6. marche.

4 1, 2, 4, 5, 7 sport individuel 3, 6 sport collectif

5 le running, le basket, le tennis

6 1. stade 2. salle de sport 3. piscine

7 2. b 3. d 4. a

8 1, 4, 5 vrai 2, 3 faux

9 2. Ils jouent à la marche. 3. Nous jouons à la natation.

B La musique

11 1. piano 2. batterie 3. guitare 4. violon 5. saxophone
6. harmonica 7. flûte

12 1. joue 2. piano 3. harmonica 4. chante. 5. musique.

13 Ex. : musique 1. batterie, guitare 2. flûte, violon
3. l'harmonica, saxophone

14 (028) 1. piano 2. guitare 3. batterie 4. musicien
5. chante 6. écouter

C Les sorties culturelles

16 1. concert **2.** opéra **3.** spectacle **4.** musée **5.** théâtre

17 1. cinéma **2.** spectacle **3.** musée **4.** théâtre **5.** concerts
6. opéra

D Les activités de loisirs à la maison

19 2. e - **3.** a **4.** d **5.** c

20 (031) **1.** regarder le film à la télévision **2.** jeu vidéo
3. écouter la radio **4.** lire **5.** se reposer

BILAN

1 1. piscine **2.** courir, marche **3.** collectifs, fait
4. musiciens, violon, flûte, harmonica, chante

2 (032) **1.** Tu vas au cinéma ?
2. Vous aimez jouer de la musique ?
3. Le samedi, on ne fait pas de running.
4. On joue du violon.
5. Je cours dans un stade.
6. La marche, c'est un sport individuel ?

sorties : 1 **pratique musicale :** 2, 4 **pratique sportive :**
3, 5, 6

3 1. sortir **2.** cinéma **3.** film **4.** lire **5.** sport **6.** vélo
7. marche **8.** individuels **9.** écoute **10.** piano **11.** guitare
12. loisir **13.** lecture **14.** se reposer

CHAPITRE

6 Les relations humaines

A Les relations amicales

2 1. font la fête, anniversaire **2.** cadeau **3.** contents,
être ensemble **4.** copain, copine, bar **5.** embrassent

3 1. anniversaire **2.** bar **3.** copains **4.** cadeau

4 1. adore **2.** bar **3.** amis **4.** faire la fête **5.** copine
6. contente

B Les relations formelles

6 1. reçoit **2.** voisin **3.** voisine **4.** apportent

7 1. fête **2.** invités **3.** apporter

C Des expressions utiles
dans les relations

9 1. Bonne année **2.** Bonne soirée **3.** Bonjour – Salut
4. Au revoir – à demain **5.** merci

10 (037) **1.** b **2.** a **3.** b **4.** a

11 salutations : 1, 4, 5, 6, 7 **souhaits :** 2, 3, 8

12 1. Bonjour **2.** À demain **3.** Bonjour **4.** Bienvenue
5. Bonne journée **6.** Au revoir

13 2. c **3.** a **4.** a **5.** c **6.** b **7.** b

BILAN

1 1. copine **2.** anniversaire **3.** recevoir **4.** amis **5.** allez
6. voisins **7.** bonsoir

2 1. d'amis **2.** bar **3.** fêtent **4.** l'anniversaire **5.** copain

---

6. collègues **7.** s'embrassent **8.** contents

3 (038) – Demain, on va **faire la fête (1)** au bureau !
– Bonne idée, pourquoi ?
– C'est l'**anniversaire (2)** du directeur, et tous les
collègues sont **invités (3)**.
– Bien. **Bonne soirée (4)** et à **demain (5)**.

4 1. Salut **2.** ça va **3.** ensemble **4.** invite **5.** fête
6. voisins **7.** apporter **8.** Bonne journée

CHAPITRE

7 L'être humain

A Le corps

2 2. la jambe **3.** le genou **4.** la tête **5.** la main **6.** le
ventre **7.** le pied **8.** le doigt

3 1. tête **2.** dos **3.** main **4.** doigt **5.** ventre **6.** jambe
7. genou **8.** bras

4 1. Elle a les pieds sur une chaise. **2.** Elle a la jambe
cassée. **3.** Elle compte avec les doigts. **4.** Il tourne la
tête. **5.** Elle porte un sac sur le dos. **6.** Il a mal au
ventre. **7.** Il a un bébé dans les bras.

6 1. dessine **2.** marchent **3.** tient **4.** écrit **5.** lève, baisse

7 Bras et mains : 2, 3, 5, 6 **Jambes et pieds :** 2, 4, 5, 6

8 1. couché **2.** debout **3.** s'assoit **4.** assis **5.** lève

9 1. assis **2.** debout **3.** se coucher **4.** s'asseoir **5.** couché

B La tête

11 1. oreille **2.** bouche **3.** cheveux **4.** nez **5.** dents
6. langue

12 1. œil **2.** nez **3.** oreille **4.** bouche **5.** langue **6.** dents
7. yeux

13 2. f **3.** d **4.** b **5.** e **6.** c

14 1. écouter **2.** regarder **3.** parler **4.** embrasser
5. manger **6.** goûter

15 1. oreilles **2.** tête **3.** nez **4.** yeux **5.** bouche **6.** langue

C La description physique

17 Ex. petit **1.** vieille **2.** gros, mince **3.** jeune

18 a : 2, 3, 4 **b :** 2, 5

19 1. pesez **2.** mesure / fait **3.** fait **4.** pèses / mesures

21 1. Chloé **2.** Daphné **3.** José **4.** Louis

22 descriptions impossibles : 1, 3, 5, 7, 8

BILAN

1 (044) **1.** les cheveux **2.** les mains **3.** les yeux **4.** le
pied **5.** le nez **6.** les doigts **7.** le dos **8.** les oreilles
9. les bras **10.** la bouche **11.** les jambes **12.** le ventre

corps : 2, 4, 6, 7, 9, 11, 12 **tête :** 1, 3, 5, 8, 10

2 1. cheveux **2.** dents **3.** doigts **4.** yeux **5.** jambes

3 1. Il marche. **2.** Elle écoute. **3.** Elle est assise. **4.** Il
écrit. **5.** Elle lève les bras. **6.** Il regarde.

4 (045) **1.** Je fais 1m 76 et 55 kilos. Je suis blond et j'ai
les yeux bleus.

2. Je mesure 1m65 et pèse 75 kilos. J'ai les cheveux bruns et les yeux verts.

3. Je suis rousse et j'ai les yeux marron. Je mesure 1m55 et pèse 46 kilos.

4. J'ai les cheveux blancs et les yeux bleus. Je fais 1m58 et 60 kilos.

5. Je fais 62 kilos et je mesure 1m78. J'ai les cheveux roux et les yeux marron.

6. Je mesure 1m56 et je pèse 52 kilos. J'ai les yeux marron et je suis blonde.

Oui : 1, 2 **Non :** 3, 4, 5, 6

CHAPITRE

8 La santé

A Les maladies

2 **1.** de la fièvre **2.** prend un médicament **3.** un rhume **4.** mal au dos

3 la malade : 2, 5, 8 le médecin : 3, 4, 6, 7

4 (047) **1.** Elle a mal où ?

2. Vous êtes malade ?

3. Elle a mal aux oreilles.

4. Tu as mal au ventre ?

5. Il est malade.

6. J'ai mal aux dents.

mal : 1, 3, 4, 6 malade : 2, 5

5 **1.** Elle a mal au dos. **2.** Tu as de la fièvre. **3.** Il a mal aux dents. **4.** Elle a mal aux oreilles. **5.** Elles sont malades.

B Les professions et les lieux de santé

7 **1.** chirurgien **2.** infirmier **3.** pompiers **4.** médecin

8 **1.** dentiste **2.** pompiers **3.** chirurgien **4.** infirmier

9 **1.** le dentiste **2.** le chirurgien **3.** l'opération **4.** le pharmacien **5.** les pompiers **6.** l'opération **7.** le pharmacien

10 **2.** d **3.** a **4.** c

11 (049) **1.** L'infirmière vient ce soir.

2. Les pompiers sont là !

4. Le cabinet médical est fermé.

7. Il est chirurgien ou médecin ?

8. Ils doivent aller aux urgences.

1, 2, 4, 7, 8

12 logiques : 1, 4, 5, 6 pas logiques : 2, 3

BILAN

❶ **1.** J'ai mal au ventre. **2.** Je vais au cabinet médical. **3.** Le médecin m'examine. **4.** Le médecin me donne une ordonnance. **5.** Je vais à la pharmacie. **6.** Le pharmacien me donne des médicaments. **7.** Je prends les médicaments pendant 4 jours.

❷ **1.** fièvre **2.** consultation **3.** malade **4.** médecin **5.** ordonnance **6.** pharmacie **7.** infirmière

❸ (050) Au **cabinet** (1) médical
– Bonjour, docteur.

– Bonjour. **Qu'est-ce qui ne va pas** (2) ?
– J'ai de la **fièvre** (3) : 39°
À la **pharmacie** (4)
– Bonjour, voici mon **ordonnance** (5).
– Voilà vos **médicaments** (6).
– Merci.
Au **laboratoire** (7)
– Voici les résultats de vos **analyses** (8).
– Merci.

CHAPITRE

9 Le logement

A L'appartement et la maison

2 **1.** porte **2.** fenêtre **3.** étages **4.** appartement **5.** escalier **6.** ascenseur

3 vrai : 2, 6, 7 faux : 1, 3, 4, 5

4 **2.** a **3.** b **4.** b

B Les pièces

6 **1.** toilettes **2.** chambre **3.** salle de bains **4.** séjour

7 (053) **1.** Notre appartement a quatre pièces, il y a trois **chambres** (1) et un **séjour** (2). Bien sûr, nous avons aussi une **cuisine** (3), une **salle de bains** (4) et des **toilettes** (5).

2. Moi, j'ai un studio. Il n'y a pas de **cuisine** (6), pas de **chambre** (7). Il y a une seule **pièce** (8), c'est la pièce de **vie** (9). J'ai aussi une **salle de bains** (10) avec des **toilettes** (11).

8 **2.** c **3.** b **4.** c, d **5.** c, d **6.** a, d **7.** b

C L'équipement

10 **1.** chaise **2.** lit **3.** canapé **4.** frigo **5.** étagère **6.** placard **7.** cuisinière **8.** télévision **9.** plaques de cuisson

11 **1.** le placard **2.** le frigo **3.** le canapé **4.** les étagères **5.** la table **6.** la chaise

12 **1.** une douche **2.** un frigo **3.** des plaques de cuisson **4.** les WC **5.** un réfrigérateur

13 **2.** cuisinière **3.** étagère **4.** canapé **5.** chaise **6.** placards **7.** lit **8.** télé

BILAN

❶ **1.** frigo **2.** table **3.** chaise **4.** salle de bains **5.** douche **6.** séjour **7.** canapé **8.** télé

❷ (055) **1.** J'**habite** dans un petit **appartement** neuf.

2. C'est un **studio** : une jolie **pièce** et une petite **cuisine**.

3. Il est au troisième **étage**.

4. J'ai une grande **fenêtre**.

5. J'adore mon **canapé**.

6. Il y a un **placard**.

7. Il y a aussi une belle **douche**.

❸ **1.** appartement **2.** cuisine **3.** placards **4.** pièce de vie **5.** canapé **6.** télévision **7.** chambres **8.** salle de bains

CHAPITRE

10 La ville

A Les lieux de la ville

2 1. quartier **2.** place **3.** avenue **4.** carrefour **5.** pont
6. feux **7.** rue

3 1. commissariat **2.** parking **3.** mairie **4.** école

4 espaces extérieurs : quartier, pont, place, parc.
espaces intérieurs : commissariat, mairie. **espaces extérieurs et intérieurs :** école, parking.

5 1. mairie **2.** calme **3.** rue **4.** centre-ville **5.** école
6. carrefour **7.** animé

6 vrai : 1, 3, 4, 8 **faux :** 2, 5, 6, 7

B Les transports en ville

8 1. gare, quai **2.** métro, station, quai **3.** bus, arrêt
4. taxi, station

9 1. ticket **2.** train, billet

10 moyens de transport : tramway, train, métro, taxi
lieux : station de taxi, gare, station de métro, quai,
arrêt de bus

11 2. c, e **3.** a, c, e **4.** b

12 1. métro **2.** tickets **3.** cher **4.** pratique **5.** train **6.** billet

C Les directions

14 1. monte **2.** droite **3.** continue **4.** traverse **5.** gauche

15 3. ~~Je ne prends pas le pont.~~ **5.** ~~Je reste dans la rue.~~
6. ~~Je tourne à gauche.~~

16 1. 3 **2.** 4 **3.** 6 **4.** 1 **5.** 2 **6.** 5

BILAN

1 1. le train **2.** le carrefour **3.** le métro **4.** le parking
5. la gare **6.** tout droit **7.** les feux **8.** les feux.

2 (059) – Tu habites au **centre-ville (1)**?
– Non, j'habite loin, je dois prendre le **train (2)** et le
métro (3). Et toi ?
– Moi, j'habite dans le nouveau **quartier (4)**, près du
commissariat (5). Je prends le **tramway (6)**. C'est
très **pratique (7)**.
– Quelle chance !

3 1. une station **2.** le carrefour **3.** continuez **4.** tournez **5.** bus

4 1. train **2.** Quai **3.** traversez **4.** continuez **5.** titres
de transport **6.** ticket **7.** descendez **8.** arrêt **9.** rue
10. pont **11.** continuer **12.** à droite

CHAPITRE

11 Les aliments et les boissons

A Les fruits et les légumes

2 1. orange **2.** pomme **3.** banane **4.** fraise **5.** cerise **6.** raisin

3 1. salade **2.** carotte **3.** pomme **4.** haricots **5.** concombre

4 1. carotte **2.** concombre **3.** haricots verts **4.** tomate
5. salade **6.** banane **7.** cerise **8.** orange **9.** pomme **10.** raisin

5 horizontalement : 1. orange **2.** raisin **3.** salade
4. tomate **5.** pommes **6.** haricots **verticalement :**
7. carotte **8.** banane **9.** cerise

B Les boissons

7 1. thé **2.** lait **3.** café **4.** alcool **5.** vin **6.** bière

8 1. thé **2.** vin, alcool **3.** café **4.** jus de fruits **5.** lait

9 (062) – Bonjour, vous désirez un café ?
– **Un thé** s'il vous plaît.
– Pour moi, un **café** et **de l'eau**.
– Et pour moi, **une bière**.
– Très bien !

10 1. bois **2.** bière **3.** soif **4.** café **5.** thé **6.** jus de fruits
7. eau

C Autres aliments

12 1. mouton **2.** poisson **3.** poule **4.** porc

13 1. fromage **2.** sel **3.** poivre **4.** sucre **5.** œufs **6.** pain
7. riz **8.** chocolat

14 (064) **1.** Oui, du bœuf, je veux bien ! **2.** Non merci,
pas de porc ! **3.** J'adore les pâtes. **4.** Il y a trop de sel !
5. Je n'aime pas le riz blanc.

15 1. ~~chocolat~~ **2.** ~~pain~~ **3.** ~~riz~~ **4.** ~~œufs~~ **5.** ~~poisson~~
6. ~~chocolat~~

16 (065) – Bonjour, on mange quoi aujourd'hui ?
– Du **poulet (1)** avec des haricots verts.
– Oh, j'ai très **faim (2)**. Je peux aussi avoir du **riz (3)** ?
– Bien sûr. Il y a des **pâtes (4)** aussi.
– Et des pommes de terre ?
– Non. Demain, avec du **bœuf (5)**.
– Et on a du **fromage (6)** ?
– Bien sûr ! Et aussi une crème au **chocolat (7)** ! Bon
appétit !
– Merci.

BILAN

1 1. tomates **2.** poulet **3.** haricots verts **4.** lait **5.** chocolat
6. œufs **7.** sucre **8.** fraises **9.** pain

2 fruits : banane, fraise, citron, cerise, pomme
légumes : tomate, carotte, haricots verts, concombre,
salade **boissons :** vin, thé, lait, café, eau **viande :** poulet,
porc, mouton, bœuf **autres aliments :** pain, sucre, sel,
œufs, poivre

3 (066) Odile : pour moi, du poisson et du riz, le gâteau
au chocolat et du vin.
Didier : je préfère du poulet et des haricots verts, des
fraises et de l'eau.
Caroline : alors, poulet riz, pour moi, et fraises, avec de l'eau.
Émile : heu… pour moi, poulet haricots verts, fraises et
un verre de vin.
Béatrice : alors, le poisson avec le riz, et le gâteau au
chocolat et… de l'eau.
Frédo : pour moi, poisson haricots verts, fraises et du vin.
Gustave : pour moi, le poulet avec du riz, et du gâteau
au chocolat, et du vin.

Odile : poison, riz, gâteau au chocolat, vin
Didier : poulet, haricots verts, fraises, eau
Caroline : poulet, riz, fraises, eau
Émile : poulet, haricots verts, fraises, vin
Béatrice : poisson, riz, gâteau au chocolat, eau
Frédo : poisson, riz, gâteau au chocolat, eau
Gustave : poulet, riz, gâteau au chocolat, vin

CHAPITRE 12 Les repas à la maison et au restaurant

A Les repas et la table

2 **2.** a, c **3.** d, e

3 **1.** couteau **2.** assiette **3.** fourchette **4.** petite cuillère
5. plat **6.** verre **7.** serviette **8.** bouteille

4 **1.** b **2.** b **3.** a **4.** b **5.** b **6.** a **7.** a

5 (068) **1.** On met quelles cuillères ? **2.** Les assiettes rouges ? **3.** Les couteaux, à droite ou à gauche ? **4.** Je mets des tasses ? **5.** Tu veux une assiette ronde ?

6 **1.** dîner **2.** fourchette **3.** cuillère **4.** déjeuner **5.** verre **6.** couteau **7.** repas **8.** assiette **9.** serviette

B Le restaurant

8 **1.** entrée **2.** plat **3.** dessert

9 **1.** mangent **2.** boivent **3.** réserve, une table **4.** l'addition

10 (070) – On va au restaurant ce soir ?
– D'accord. Je **réserve (1)** une **table (2)** ! Tu veux **manger (3)** quoi ?
– Un super **plat (4)** !
– D'accord. Et l'**addition (5)**, c'est pour moi !
– Mais non, je **paie/paye (6)** !

11 **2.** regarder la carte **3.** choisir un plat ou un menu **4.** manger et boire **5.** payer

12 **1.** le menu **2.** une boisson **3.** un café **4.** le plat **5.** du sel

13 **serveur :** 3, 4, 9 **client :** 1, 2, 5, 6, 7, 8

14 **1.** addition **2.** boisson **3.** entrée **4.** réserver **5.** carte **6.** plat

BILAN

1 **1.** carte **2.** addition **3.** client **4.** réserver **5.** menu

2 **1.** réserver **2.** table **3.** déjeuner **4.** dîner

3 (071) – Qu'est-ce qu'il y a dans le **menu (1)** à 13 euros ?
– Une **entrée (2)**, un **plat (3)** et un **dessert (4)**.
– C'est parfait.
– Et vous voulez une **boisson (5)** ?
– Oui, je vais prendre une **bouteille (6)** d'**eau (7)** gazeuse, s'il vous plaît.
– Très bien.
– Excusez-moi, j'ai une **fourchette (8)** mais je n'ai pas de **couteau (9)**.
– Je vous en apporte un toute de suite.

4 **1.** restaurant, choisis, menu **2.** prépares, repas **3.** voulez, couteau, cuillère **4.** boit, verre, petit-déjeuner **5.** demande, addition, paie **6.** prendre, dessert, dîner

CHAPITRE 13 Les commerces

A Les magasins

2 **1.** boutique **2.** supermarché **3.** centre commercial **4.** marché

3 **1.** pharmacie **2.** laverie **3.** pâtisserie **4.** boulangerie

4 **1.** boutique **2.** pâtisserie **3.** marché **4.** magasin **5.** pharmacie **6.** supermarché **7.** laverie

5 **1.** boucherie **2.** pâtisserie **3.** pharmacie, supermarché **4.** marché, supermarché

B Les achats

7 **1.** euro **2.** prix **3.** carte bancaire **4.** espèces, argent

8 **2.** c **3.** a **4.** c **5.** a **6.** b **7.** c **8.** b **9.** c

9 **le client :** 1, 2, 4, 5 **le vendeur :** 3, 6, 7

BILAN

1 (074) **1.** laverie **2.** pharmacie **3.** boulangerie **4.** supermarché **5.** espèces **6.** payer **7.** cliente **8.** chèque

2 **1.** boulangerie **2.** combien **3.** billet **4.** pharmacie **5.** coûte **6.** euros **7.** cher **8.** boutique de vêtements **9.** prix **10.** payer **11.** carte

3 **horizontalement :** **1.** prix **2.** carte **3.** argent **4.** billet **verticalement :** **5.** laverie **6.** payer **7.** euro **8.** cher **9.** marché **10.** client

CHAPITRE 14 Les vêtements

A Les vêtements

2 **1.** veste **2.** jupe **3.** manteau **4.** chaussures **5.** tee-shirt **6.** pantalon **7.** chemise **8.** robe **9.** pull **10.** chaussettes **11.** bottes

3 **1.** Kian **2.** Carine **3.** Nathanaël

4 **1.** chemise **2.** un manteau **3.** un jean **4.** des chaussettes **5.** un pantalon **6.** un pull

5 (076) **1.** N'oubliez pas vos chaussures. **2.** Tu as ton jean ? **3.** Où sont vos chaussettes ? **4.** Deux pantalons, Élodie, ça va ? **5.** Et ta jupe noire ? **6.** Quatre tee-shirts, c'est bien ! **7.** Coralie, tu prends une veste ?

6 **1.** mettre **2.** enlever **3.** mettre **4.** essayer **5.** enlever

B Les accessoires

8 **1.** ceinture **2.** parapluie **3.** sac à main **4.** lunettes de soleil **5.** écharpe **6.** sac à dos **7.** gants

9 **1.** un parapluie **2.** des gants **3.** une ceinture **4.** un chapeau **5.** des lunettes **6.** un sac

10 **1.** le parapluie **2.** le sac à dos **3.** l'écharpe **4.** les lunettes

C Les couleurs et les matières

12 **1.** bleu **2.** jaune **3.** blanc **4.** noir **5.** vert **6.** orange **7.** gris **8.** rose

13 vrai : 1, 4, 5, 6 faux : 2, 3

14 **2.** noir **3.** orange **4.** bleu **5.** vert **6.** rouge **7.** jaune **8.** rose

15 **1.** laine **2.** coton **3.** laine **4.** cuir **5.** coton

16 **1.** un tee-shirt en coton **2.** un parapluie **3.** des lunettes de soleil **4.** un parapluie **5.** un manteau en laine. **6.** une veste en cuir

BILAN

① (079) **Anna :** un pull, une écharpe, un pantalon, un tee-shirt, des bottes, un sac à dos
David : un manteau, des chaussettes, des chaussures, un pantalon, une ceinture

② **1.** essayer **2.** chaussures **3.** bleues **4.** sac **5.** cuir **6.** mettre **7.** robe **8.** Verte **9.** gants **10.** blancs **11.** pantalon **12.** noir **13.** veste

③ **1.** chaussures en cuir **2.** manteau gris **3.** chaussettes en laine **4.** sac à main en cuir. **5.** robe jaune.

CHAPITRE
15 La poste et la banque

A La poste

2 **1.** boîte aux lettres **2.** courrier **3.** colis **4.** lettre **5.** carte postale **6.** enveloppe **7.** timbre

3 **1.** une lettre **2.** reçoit **3.** l'adresse sur une enveloppe

4 **1.** enveloppe **2.** boîte aux lettres **3.** code postal **4.** adresse **5.** poste **6.** envoyer **7.** courrier **8.** timbre **9.** carte postale

5 **1.** enveloppe **2.** colis **3.** envoyer **4.** timbre **5.** recevoir une carte postale **6.** la boîte aux lettres.

6 (081) – Je vais envoyer une **carte postale (1)** à Brahim. Tu peux me donner son **adresse (2)** ?
– 15 rue Beaubourg
– Et le **code postal (3)** ?
– 75003. Tu veux une **enveloppe (4)** ?
– Oui, et tu as un **timbre (5)** aussi ?
– Non, tu dois aller à la **poste (6)**.
– Le **courrier (7)** part quand ?
– Cet après-midi ou demain.

B La banque

8 **1.** banque **2.** carte bancaire **3.** chèque **4.** distributeur **5.** espèces **6.** compte bancaire **7.** changer **8.** retirer

9 **1.** euros **2.** des espèces **3.** d'argent **4.** au distributeur **5.** une carte bancaire **6.** carte bancaire **7.** distributeur **8.** billets

10 (083) **1.** On va passer au **distributeur (1)**.
2. Tu as de l'**argent (2)** ?
3. Vous avez un **compte (3)** ici ?
4. J'ai un **billet (4)** de 200 euros.
5. On va **changer (5)** notre argent.
6. Nous ne pouvons pas accepter ce **chèque (6)**.
7. Ils refusent les **espèces (7)**.
8. Elle doit **retirer (8)** 1500 euros.

11 **2.** a **3.** b **4.** e **5.** d **6.** g **7.** c

12 **2.** distributeur **3.** espèces **4.** compte **5.** billet **6.** retirer **7.** banque **8.** changer **9.** argent

BILAN

① **1.** adresse **2.** argent **3.** espèces **4.** colis **5.** timbre **6.** compte **7.** distributeur **8.** chèque **9.** lettre **10.** billet

② (084) **1.** Bonjour madame, je voudrais envoyer un colis.
2. J'ai un rendez-vous pour ouvrir un compte.
3. Vous voulez retirer de l'argent ?
4. Pour envoyer cette carte postale au Japon, c'est combien ?
5. Un carnet de timbres ? Voilà !
6. Excusez-moi, je voudrais changer 150 dollars.
7. Je voudrais des enveloppes, s'il vous plaît.

à la poste : 1, 4, 5, 7   **à la banque :** 2, 3, 6

③ **1.** poste **2.** colis **3.** adresse **4.** timbres **5.** un billet **6.** Banque **7.** Retirer **8.** espèces **9.** distributeur **10.** carte **11.** changer

CHAPITRE
16 Le téléphone et le numérique

A Le téléphone

2 **1.** écran **2.** applications **3.** chargeur pour recharger **4.** carte SIM **5.** numéro de téléphone

3 **1.** application **2.** envoie **3.** répond **4.** numéro **5.** laisse un message **6.** recharger

4 (086) – Je dois téléphoner à Rachid mais je n'ai pas mon **téléphone (1)**.
– Tiens, voilà mon **smartphone (2)**.
– Je peux **envoyer (3)** un **SMS (4)** ?
– Oui, bien sûr !
– Et il peut **laisser (5)** un **message (6)** ?
– Pas de problème, il connait mon **numéro (7)** !

5 **1.** SIM **2.** le chargeur **3.** l'écran **4.** portable

B Le numérique

7 **1.** tablette **2.** souris **3.** clé USB **4.** clavier **5.** site Internet **6.** mél

8 **1.** souris **2.** tablettes **3.** clés usb **4.** méls **5.** sites

9 **1.** clique **2.** télécharge **3.** enregistre

10 **1.** site **2.** cliquez **3.** souris **4.** enregistrez **5.** clé USB **6.** éteignez

11 **1.** réseaux sociaux **2.** poste, commentaires **3.** mot de passe

12 **2.** f **3.** b **4.** a **5.** e **6.** d

13 **1.** ~~un site~~ **2.** ~~J'enregistre~~ **3.** ~~un site~~ **4.** ~~un site~~ **5.** ~~cliquer~~ **6.** ~~ce mél~~ **7.** ~~son site~~ **8.** ~~éteindre~~

14 (088) mot de passe – enregistrer – clavier – télécharger – éteindre – clé USB

BILAN

① **1.** clavier **2.** smartphone **3.** écran **4.** souris **5.** messages **6.** chargeur **7.** numéro

2 (089) **1.** Je vais allumer mon ordinateur
2. Il est vieux, ton clavier !
3. On a oublié d'enregistrer les documents.
4. Je n'ai pas mon chargeur.
5. Je vous envoie le mél demain.
6. Je ne veux pas cliquer trop vite.
7. Il faut éteindre votre ordinateur.
8. Regarde, j'ai un SMS de Fabien.
9. Je vais lui laisser un message.
10. On voudrait télécharger ce document.

3 **1.** ordinateurs **2.** tablettes **3.** internet **4.** smartphones **5.** claviers **6.** clés USB

_{CHAPITRE}
17 La nature et le temps qu'il fait

A La nature

2 **1.** forêt **2.** arbre **3.** montagne **4.** fleurs **5.** Campagne **6.** ciel **7.** rivière **8.** mer

3 **1.** mer **2.** fleurs **3.** nature **4.** forêt **5.** rivière **6.** arbres **7.** paysage

4 logique : 1, 3, 6 pas logique : 2, 4, 5

5 (091) **1. Chiara :** J'habite à la **campagne**. De ma chambre, je vois une **forêt** avec des **arbres** magnifiques.
2. Jörg : Moi, je suis à la **montagne**, loin de la **rivière**, mais dans la **nature** où il y a beaucoup de **fleurs** de toutes les couleurs en juin et juillet. Et le **ciel** est toujours très beau !

B Le temps qu'il fait

7 **1.** printemps **2.** été **3.** automne **4.** hiver

8 **2.** a **3.** b **4.** c **5.** c **6.** b **7.** d **8.** a

9 **1.** soleil **2.** nuages **3.** vent **4.** neige **5.** pluie

10 **1.** hiver **2.** nuages **3.** neige **4.** printemps **5.** soleil **6.** automne **7.** pluie **8.** été **9.** saison **10.** météo

11 **1.** froid. **2.** neige **3.** chaud **4.** beau **5.** pleut

12 **1.** Il y a beaucoup de vent. **2.** Il y a du soleil. **3.** Il neige. **4.** Il y a des nuages. **5.** Le soleil est magnifique.

13 **2.** printemps **3.** neige **4.** soleil **5.** hiver **6.** nuages **7.** vent **8.** automne

14 (093) « Bonjour à toutes et tous ! Premier jour de l'été ! Quel **temps (1)** fait-il aujourd'hui ? Voici nos prévisions. Attention aux **orages (2)** à Lyon. Il y a beaucoup de **nuages (3)**, de **vent (4)** et il fait **chaud (5)**.
Une situation très différente à Lille : il fait **beau (6)** et **chaud (7)**, le **soleil (8)** est magnifique ; c'est sûr, l'**hiver (9)** est terminé dans le nord de la France ! »

BILAN

1 pour décrire la nature : Il y a une rivière. C'est la mer. Il y a des montagnes. Il y a une grande forêt. La campagne est très verte. Le paysage est très beau. Il y a beaucoup de fleurs. Les arbres sont magnifiques. pour décrire le temps qu'il fait : Il y a des nuages. Il y a du soleil. Il fait beau. Il pleut. Il fait froid. Il fait mauvais. Il neige. Il fait chaud.

2 (094) **1.** Jean Ferrat : La **montagne**.
2. Georges Brassens : Auprès de mon **arbre**.
3. Édith Piaf : Sous le **ciel** de Paris.
4. Charles Trenet : La **mer**.
5. Garou et Céline Dion : Sous le **vent**
6. Bénabar : La **forêt**.
7. Cali : Je rêve de voir l'**été**
8. Orelsan : La **pluie**

3 **1.** En automne, les arbres. **2.** beau, nuages **3.** printemps, arbres, fleurs, campagne. **4.** une forêt, arbres. **5.** beau, campagne. **6.** ciel, nuages **7.** paysages, fleurs

_{CHAPITRE}
18 Le voyage et les vacances

A Le voyage

2 **1.** avion **2.** gare **3.** train **4.** car **5.** bagages **6.** sac **7.** valise

3 **1.** ~~bagages~~ **2.** ~~aéroport~~ **3.** ~~avion~~ **4.** ~~gare~~ **5.** ~~bateau~~

4 **1.** aller **2.** part **3.** départ **4.** arrive **5.** retour **6.** arrivée

5 (096) Sarah : Tu dois réserver ton **billet (1)** pour le retour ?
Dylan : Non, j'ai acheté un **aller-retour (2)**.
Sarah : Super ! Le **départ (3)** du **train (4)** est à 7h15.
Dylan : On se donne rendez-vous à la **gare (5)** ?
Sarah : Oui, d'accord. Je prends un **sac (6)**, pas de **valise (7)**. Et toi ?
Dylan : Je ne sais pas encore, mais un petit **bagage (8)**, c'est sûr.

6 **1.** ~~Vous attendez la gare.~~ **2.** ~~Nous ne réservons pas l'information.~~ **3.** ~~Le départ est complet.~~ **4.** ~~Monsieur, c'est votre aller ?~~ **5.** ~~L'aller-retour est à 6h37.~~ **6.** ~~Je voudrais une arrivée pour Nice.~~ **7.** ~~Écoute, ils annoncent le billet.~~ **8.** ~~Tu connais l'heure d'arrivée de l'aéroport ?~~

7 **1.** vol **2.** avion **3.** complet **4.** réserver **5.** billet **6.** gare **7.** arrivée **8.** train **9.** sac **10.** Valise

B Les lieux et les logements de vacances

9 **1.** hôtel **2.** clé **3.** chambre **4.** camping **5.** tente **6.** location

10 **2.** b **3.** c **4.** g **5.** d **6.** a **7.** e

11 (098) **1.** On a une grande **chambre**.
2. Je prends ma **clé** à la **réception**.
3. Il fait froid sous la **tente**.
4. Comment est votre **location** ?
5. Nous sommes dans un **camping** près de la mer.

12 **1.** loué **2.** réserver **3.** chambre **4.** hôtel **5.** camping **6.** tente

13 **2.** camping **3.** location **4.** clé **5.** hôtel **6.** réception **7.** tente

BILAN

1 (099) **1.** À quelle heure est ton vol ?
2. Je ne trouve pas mon sac.
3. Il a la chambre 24.
4. On attend le train.
5. Je suis à l'aéroport.
6. Je vais faire ma valise.

7. Je ne sais pas où est ma clé.

8. J'arrive à la gare.

9. On est à la réception.

10. Ils ont trop de bagages.

avion : 1, 5 **hôtel :** 3, 7, 9 **gare :** 4, 8 **bagages :** 2, 6, 10

2 **le client :** 2, 4 **l'employé :** 1, 3, 5, 6, 7, 8

3 **1.** camping **2.** pars **3.** avion **4.** billet **5.** retour **6.** hôtel **7.** loue

CHAPITRE

19 L'école et les études

A Le matériel pour étudier

2 **1.** feuille **2.** livre **3.** page **4.** crayon **5.** stylo **6.** dictionnaire **7.** papier **8.** ordinateur **9.** tablette

3 **1.** feuilles, classeur **2.** tablette **3.** dictionnaire **4.** crayon, stylo **5.** papier

4 (101) – Baptiste, tu as quoi dans ton sac ?

– Ma tablette, mon livre, du papier et un stylo. Je ne prends pas mon dictionnaire.

– Et ton ordinateur ?

– Non, et je ne prends pas mon classeur.

dans son sac : 3, 5, 6 **pas dans son sac :** 2, 4, 7

5 **1. pour écrire :** une tablette, du papier, un crayon, une feuille, un ordinateur

pour lire : un dictionnaire, une tablette, du papier, une feuille, un ordinateur, une page

B Les lieux

7 **1.** collège **2.** lycée **3.** université

8 **1.** à l'école **2.** au collège **3.** au lycée

9 **1.** bibliothèque **2.** secrétariat **3.** cafétéria **4.** salle de cours

10 **2.** a **3.** e **4.** c **5.** d

11 (103) **1.** C'est un **lycée** moderne.

2. La **bibliothèque** est à côté du secrétariat.

3. Cette **salle de cours** est fermée aujourd'hui.

4. Le **secrétariat** est au premier étage.

5. J'ai adoré mon **université**.

6. Où est l'**école**, s'il vous plaît ?

C L'apprentissage

13 **1.** élèves **2.** apprendre **3.** professeur **4.** explique **5.** étudiante **6.** étudie **7.** prépare **8.** examen

14 **1.** le cours **2.** les élèves **3.** à l'étudiant **4.** les élèves **5.** facile **6.** passer

15 (105) – Vous êtes étudiante ?

– Oui, et je **passe (1)** mon dernier **examen (2)** demain !

– Bon. Vous allez **réussir (3)**.

– J'espère ! Si je **réussis (4)**, je vais être **professeur (5)**, je vais donner des **cours (6)** !

– Alors, bonne chance !

BILAN

1 **1.** étudiant **2.** cours **3.** élèves **4.** lycée **5.** examens

2 (106) **1.** On va à la **bibliothèque**.

2. Tu as ton **ordinateur** ?

3. Elle va **passer** un **examen** la semaine prochaine.

4. Mon collège est près de la maison.

5. J'ai oublié mon **classeur**.

6. Cet exercice n'est pas **facile**.

3 **1.** crayon **2.** lycée **3.** Université **4.** pages **5.** professeur **6.** élèves **7.** cours **8.** examen

4 **le professeur :** 2, 3, 5, 8, 10 **l'étudiant :** 1, 4, 6, 7, 9

CHAPITRE

20 Le travail

A Les professions

2 **1.** ingénieur **2.** journaliste **3.** médecin **4.** agriculteur **5.** chauffeur **6.** policière **7.** pompier **8.** actrice **9.** commerçant **10.** garagiste **11.** photographe

3 **1.** acteur **2.** avocat **3.** médecin **4.** agricultrice **5.** policier **6.** ingénieure **7.** chauffeur

4 **1.** b,c **2.** a,d **3.** e,f **4.** g, h

5 (108) – Élise, tu veux faire quoi, plus tard ?

– Moi, je voudrais être **médecin (1)** ou **ingénieure (2)**. C'est très différent, je sais. Et toi, Amir ?

– Moi, je veux être à l'extérieur. **Photographe (3)**, j'aimerais bien. Mais ce n'est pas facile. Alors, **policier (4)**, pourquoi pas ?

– Ce n'est pas du tout la même chose ! Moi, je serai **commerçante (5)** ! C'est sûr !

– Moi, j'adore conduire ! Je serai **chauffeur (6)** et, si ce n'est pas possible, **garagiste (7)**. Ou alors, comme mon père : **journaliste (8)**

– Rendez-vous dans 10 ans !

B L'entreprise

7 **1.** bureau **2.** directeur **3.** assistant **4.** employé

8 **vrai :** 3, 4, 5 **faux :** 1, 2

9 (110) **1.** Elle est **assistante**, elle veut devenir **directrice**.

2. Vous êtes au **chômage** ? Vous pouvez **suivre** une **formation**.

3. On **cherche** un travail dans une **entreprise** française.

10 **1.** entreprise **2.** assistante **3.** directeur **4.** au chômage **5.** suivre **6.** formation

BILAN

1 **1.** cherchez **2.** travailler **3.** entreprise **4.** assistant **5.** directeur **6.** collègues **7.** suivre

2 (111) **1.** Amélie travaille dans un **bureau**.

2. Gaëlle a un bon **travail**.

3. Karine est au **chômage**.

4. Kadder est **journaliste**.

5. Tiago est **employé** chez un **commerçant**.

6. Sonia est **actrice**.

7. Janeck **travaille** dans l'**entreprise** XLAB

3 **1.** agriculteur **2.** ingénieur **3.** policier **4.** collègue **5.** médecin **6.** employé **7.** bureau

INDEX GÉNÉRAL

Les numéros renvoient aux chapitres.

une fenêtre **9**

la fête **6**

(faire) la fête **6**

un feu / les feux **10**

une feuille **19**

février **1**

une fiche d'inscription **1**

la fièvre **8**

(avoir de la) fièvre **8**

une fille **3**

un film **5**

un fils **3**

une fleur **17**

une flûte **5**

le football **5**

une forêt **17**

une formation **20**

une fourchette **12**

une fraise **11**

un frère **3**

un frigo **19**

(il fait) froid **17**

le fromage **11**

un fruit **11**

G

les gants (*m*) **14**

un(e) garagiste **20**

la gare **10, 18**

à gauche **10**

un genou **7**

goûter **17**

grand(e) **17**

la grand-mère **3**

le grand-père **3**

gris(e) **14**

gros / grosse **17**

la guitare **5**

la gymnastique **5**

H

habiter **9**

les haricots verts **11**

un harmonica **5**

une heure **2**

(être à) l'heure **2**

hier **2**

l'hiver (m) **17**

un homme **1**

un hôpital **8**

un horaire **2**

une horloge **2**

un hôtel **18**

I

un immeuble **9**

un infirmier / une infirmière **8**

un(e) ingénieur(e) **20**

Internet **16**

une invitation **6**

un(e) invité(e) **6**

(être) invité(e) **6**

J

la jambe **7**

janvier **1**

jaune **14**

un jean **14**

un jeu **5**

un jeu vidéo **5**

jeudi **2**

jeune **7**

jouer **5**

jouer à + nom d'un sport **5**

jouer de + nom d'un instrument **5**

un jour **2**

(il fait) jour **2**

un(e) journaliste **20**

une journée **2**

juillet **1**

juin **1**

une jupe **14**

un jus de fruit **11**

L

le laboratoire **8**

la laine **14**

S

T

INDEX THÉMATIQUE

1 L'identité

	Traduction dans ma langue
une adresse	
l'âge (*m*)	
un an	
une année	
l'année de naissance	
août	
une avenue	
avril	
une carte d'étudiant	
une carte d'identité	
le code postal	
une date	
la date de naissance	
décembre	
une femme	
février	
une fiche d'inscription	
un homme	
janvier	
juillet	
juin	
le lieu de naissance	
madame	
mai	
mars	
un mois	
monsieur	
la nationalité	
né(e), être né(e)	
un nom	
le nom de famille	
novembre	

Traduction dans ma langue

un numéro	....
octobre	....
un passeport	....
un pays	....
un permis de conduire	....
une place	....
prénom	....
une rue	....
septembre	....
le sexe féminin	....
le sexe masculin	....
un titre de séjour	....
une ville	....

2 Les moments de la journée, l'heure et les jours de la semaine

un(e) après-midi	....
aujourd'hui	....
être en avance	....
demain	....
il est une heure et demie	....
dimanche	....
une heure	....
être à l'heure	....
hier	....
un horaire	....
une horloge	....
jeudi	....
un jour	....
il fait jour	....
une journée	....

Traduction dans ma langue

lundi	....
mardi	....
un matin	....
mercredi	....
midi	....
minuit	....
une minute	....
une montre	....
la nuit	....
il fait nuit	....
il est une heure et quart	....
un rendez-vous	....
avoir rendez-vous	....
être en retard	....
samedi	....
une seconde	....
une semaine	....
un soir	....
vendredi	....

3 La famille

célibataire	....
un copain / une copine	....
un couple	....
divorcé(e)	....
les enfants	....
la famille	....
la femme	....
la fille	....
le fils	....
le frère	....
le grand-père	....
la grand-mère	....

le mari ....

marié(e) ....

la mère ....

pacsé(e) ....

les parents ....

le père ....

la sœur ....

séparé(e) ....

veuf, veuve ....

vivre avec ....

vivre seul ....

vivre en couple ....

vivre ensemble ....

4 La vie quotidienne

une brosse à dents ....

se brosser les dents ....

se coiffer ....

se coucher ....

faire les courses ....

faire la cuisine ....

déjeuner ....

le dentifrice ....

dîner ....

dormir ....

une douche ....

prendre une douche ....

se doucher ....

se laver ....

se lever ....

faire le ménage ....

le petit déjeuner ....

prendre le petit déjeuner ....

	Traduction dans ma langue
se raser	....
un rasoir	....
se réveiller	....
le savon	....
une serviette	....
le shampoing	....
travailler	....

5 Les loisirs

le basket	....
la batterie	....
chanter	....
le cinéma	....
un concert	....
courir	....
écouter	....
l'équitation	....
un film	....
la flûte	....
le football	....
la guitare	....
la gymnastique	....
l'harmonica	....
un jeu	....
un jeu vidéo	....
jouer	....
jouer à + *nom d'un sport*	....
jouer de + *nom d'un instrument*	....
la lecture	....
lire	....
faire de la marche	....
un musée	....
un musicien, une musicienne	....

la musique	....
la natation	....
un opéra	....
le piano	....
une piscine	....
la radio	....
regarder	....
se reposer	....
le running	....
une salle de sport	....
le saxophone	....
sortir	....
un spectacle	....
le sport	....
un sport individuel	....
un sport collectif	....
faire du sport	....
un stade	....
la télévision	....
le tennis	....
le théâtre	....
le vélo	....
le violon	....
visiter	....

6 Les relations humaines

adorer	....
un(e) ami(e)	....
une année	....
bonne année	....
un anniversaire	....
apporter	....
au revoir	....

Traduction dans ma langue

un bar	....
à bientôt	....
bienvenue	....
bonjour	....
bonsoir	....
un cadeau	....
content(e)	....
un copain / une copine	....
coucou	....
demain	....
à demain	....
embrasser	....
être ensemble	....
la fête	....
faire la fête	....
une invitation	....
un(e) invité(e)	....
être invité(e)	....
merci	....
recevoir un ami	....
recevoir un cadeau	....
salut	....
une soirée	....
bonne soirée	....
un(e) voisin(e)	....
un week-end	....
bon week-end	....

7 L'être humain

s'asseoir	....
être assis(e)	....
baisser (la tête,...)	....
blanc / blanche	....

bleu(e)	....
blond(e)	....
la bouche	....
le bras	....
brun(e)	....
les cheveux	....
le corps	....
être couché(e)	....
se coucher	....
courir	....
court(e)	....
être debout	....
une dent	....
dessiner	....
un doigt	....
le dos	....
écouter	....
écrire	....
embrasser	....
faire 1m70	....
faire 55 kilos	....
le genou	....
goûter	....
grand(e)	....
gros / grosse	....
la jambe	....
jeune	....
la langue	....
lever (la jambe,..)	....
long / longue	....
la main	....
manger	....
marcher	....

Traduction dans ma langue

marron ....

mesurer ....

mince ....

le nez ....

un œil / les yeux ....

l'oreille ....

parler ....

peser ....

petit(e) ....

le pied ....

le poids ....

regarder ....

respirer ....

roux / rousse ....

la taille ....

tenir ....

la tête ....

le ventre ....

vert(e) ....

vieux / vieille ....

8 Les relations humaines

une analyse ....

le cabinet médical ....

un chirurgien / une chirurgienne ....

une consultation ....

un dentiste ....

un examen ....

la fièvre ....

avoir de la fièvre ....

un hôpital ....

un infirmier / une infirmière ....

un laboratoire ....

avoir mal à ....

un malade ....

être malade ....

un médecin ....

un médicament ....

une opération ....

une ordonnance ....

une pharmacie ....

un pompier / une pompière ....

prendre un médicament ....

une radio ....

un rhume ....

avoir un / le rhume ....

les urgences ....

9 Le logement

ancien / ancienne ....

un appartement ....

un ascenseur ....

un canapé ....

une chaise ....

une chambre ....

une cuisine ....

une cuisinière ....

une douche ....

un escalier ....

un étage ....

une étagère ....

une fenêtre ....

un frigo ....

habiter ....

un immeuble ....

un lit ....

Traduction dans ma langue

une maison ....

neuf / neuve ....

une pièce ....

une pièce de vie ....

un placard ....

des plaques de cuisson ....

une porte ....

un réfrigérateur ....

une salle de bains ....

un séjour ....

un studio ....

une table ....

une télévision, une télé, une TV ....

les WC, les toilettes ....

10 La ville

animé(e) ....

un arrêt de bus ....

une avenue ....

un billet ....

le bus ....

calme ....

un carrefour ....

le centre-ville ....

le commissariat ....

continuer ....

descendre ....

tout droit ....

à droite ....

une école ....

les feux ....

une gare ....

à gauche ....

une mairie ....

le métro ....

monter ....

un parc ....

un parking ....

une place ....

un pont ....

pratique ....

un quai ....

un quartier ....

rapide ....

une rue ....

une station de taxi ....

un taxi ....

un ticket ....

un titre de transport ....

tourner ....

le train ....

le tramway ....

traverser ....

11 Les aliments et les boissons

l'alcool ....

avoir faim ....

avoir soif ....

une banane ....

la bière ....

le bœuf ....

boire ....

le café ....

une carotte ....

une cerise ....

le chocolat ....

Traduction dans ma langue

un citron	....
un concombre	....
l'eau	....
une fraise	....
le fromage	....
un fruit	....
les haricots verts	....
un jus de fruit	....
le lait	....
un légume	....
manger	....
le mouton	....
un œuf / des œufs	....
une orange	....
le pain	....
les pâtes	....
le poisson	....
le poivre	....
une pomme	....
une pomme de terre	....
le porc	....
un poulet	....
le raisin	....
le riz	....
une salade	....
le sel	....
le sucre	....
le thé	....
une tomate	....
la viande	....
le vin	....

12 Les repas à la maison et au restaurant

l'addition	....
une assiette	....
boire	....
une boisson	....
une bouteille	....
la carte	....
un couteau	....
une cuillère	....
une petite cuillère	....
déjeuner	....
le déjeuner	....
le dessert	....
dîner	....
le dîner	....
une entrée	....
une fourchette	....
manger	....
le menu	....
payer	....
le petit déjeuner	....
le plat	....
prendre le petit-déjeuner	....
le repas	....
réserver	....
un restaurant	....
une serviette	....
la table	....
une tasse	....
un verre	....

13 Les commerces

Traduction dans ma langue

acheter	....
l'argent	....
un billet	....
la boucherie	....
la boulangerie	....
une boutique	....
une carte bancaire	....
le centre commercial	....
cher / chère	....
un(e) client(e)	....
coûter	....
les espèces	....
l'euro	....
faire un achat	....
la laverie	....
un magasin	....
le marché	....
la pâtisserie	....
payer	....
la pharmacie	....
le prix	....
le supermarché	....
un vendeur / une vendeuse	....

14 Les vêtements

blanc / blanche	....
bleu(e)	....
des bottes	....
une ceinture	....
un chapeau	....
des chaussettes	....
des chaussures	....

	Traduction dans ma langue
une chemise	....
le coton	....
en coton	....
le cuir	....
en cuir	....
une écharpe	....
enlever	....
essayer	....
des gants	....
gris(e)	....
jaune	....
un jean	....
une jupe	....
la laine	....
en laine	....
des lunettes	....
des lunettes de soleil	....
un manteau	....
mettre	....
noir(e)	....
orange	....
un pantalon	....
un parapluie	....
un pull	....
une robe	....
rose	....
rouge	....
un sac à dos	....
un sac à main	....
un tee-shirt	....
vert(e)	....
une veste	....

15 La poste et la banque | Traduction dans ma langue

une adresse ....

l'argent ....

un billet ....

une boîte aux lettres ....

une carte bancaire ....

une carte postale ....

changer de l'argent ....

un chèque ....

le code postal ....

un colis ....

un compte ....

le courrier ....

un distributeur ....

une enveloppe ....

envoyer ....

des espèces ....

une lettre ....

recevoir ....

retirer de l'argent ....

un timbre ....

16 Le téléphone et le numérique

allumer un ordinateur ....

appeler ....

une application ....

une carte SIM ....

un chargeur ....

un clavier ....

une clé USB ....

cliquer ....

un commentaire ....

un courriel ....

un document ....

un écran ....

enregistrer ....

éteindre un ordinateur ....

envoyer ....

Internet ....

laisser un message ....

un mél ....

un message ....

un mot de passe ....

un numéro de téléphone ....

un ordinateur ....

un ordinateur portable ....

poster un commentaire ....

recharger ....

répondre ....

les réseaux sociaux ....

un site ....

un smartphone ....

un SMS ....

la souris ....

une tablette ....

télécharger ....

téléphoner ....

le téléphone ....

le téléphone portable ....

17 La nature et le temps qu'il fait

Traduction dans ma langue

un arbre	....
l'automne	....
il fait beau	....
la campagne	....
il fait chaud	....
le ciel	....
l'été	....
une fleur	....
une forêt	....
il fait froid	....
l'hiver	....
il fait mauvais	....
la mer	....
la montagne	....
la nature	....
neiger	....
il neige	....
la neige	....
un nuage	....
le paysage	....
il pleut	....
pleuvoir	....
la pluie	....
le printemps	....
une rivière	....
une saison	....
le soleil	....
le vent	....

18 Le voyage et les vacances

Traduction dans ma langue

Français	Traduction dans ma langue
un aéroport	....
un aller	....
aller à la campagne	....
aller à la mer	....
aller à la montagne	....
un aller-retour	....
l'arrivée	....
arriver	....
un avion	....
les bagages	....
un bateau	....
un billet	....
le camping	....
faire du camping	....
un car	....
une chambre	....
une clé	....
c'est complet	....
le départ	....
faire une réservation	....
la gare	....
l'hôtel	....
une location	....
louer	....
partir	....
la réception	....
une réservation	....
faire une réservation	....
réserver	....

Traduction dans ma langue

le retour ....

un sac ....

une tente ....

le train ....

la valise ....

un vol ....

19 L'école et les études

apprendre ....

la bibliothèque ....

la cafétéria ....

un classeur ....

un collège ....

un cours ....

un crayon ....

un dictionnaire ....

difficile ....

une école ....

un(e) élève ....

un(e) étudiant(e) ....

étudier ....

un examen ....

expliquer ....

facile ....

une feuille ....

un livre ....

un lycée ....

un ordinateur ....

une page ....

le papier ....

passer un examen ....

préparer un examen ....

réussir un examen ....

une salle de cours ....

le secrétariat ....

un stylo ....

une tablette ....

une université ....

20 Le travail

un acteur / une actrice ....

un agriculteur / une agricultrice ....

un(e) assistant(e) ....

un(e) avocat(e) ....

un bureau ....

un(e) chauffeur(e) ....

chercher un travail ....

le chômage ....

être au chômage ....

un(e) collègue ....

un(e) commerçant(e) ....

un directeur / une directrice ....

un(e) employé(e) ....

une formation ....

suivre une formation ....

un(e) garagiste ....

un(e) ingénieur(e) ....

un(e) journaliste ....

un médecin ....

un(e) photographe ....

un policier / une policière ....

un pompier / une pompière ....

travailler ....

un travail ....

Index objectifs fonctionnels

Les numéros renvoient aux chapitres.

La prononciation des sons du français

(API : Alphabet Phonétique International)

❯ Voyelles / Sons vocaliques

[a]	madame, âge
[ə]	se lever, genou
[e]	télécharger, année, nez, rendez-vous
[ɛ]	sexe, adresse, bouteille, septembre, être, père, chaise, juillet
[i]	mardi, stylo
[o]	numéro, bureau, chaud, hôtel
[ɔ]	homme, octobre
[y]	menu, jupe, flûte
[u]	douche, goûter
[ø]	euro, bleu
[œ]	jeune, ordinateur, sœur
[ɑ̃]	client, ensemble, campagne, écran
[ɔ̃]	saison, prénom, concombre
[ɛ̃]	magasin, timbre, main, faim, éteindre, ancien
[œ̃]	un, brun, lundi,

❯ Semi-voyelles

[j]	travailler, feuille, fille, réveiller, crayon, employer
[w]	poids, voisin, bonsoir, froid

❯ Consonnes / Sons consonantiques

[b]	bar, bonjour, jambe
[ʃ]	chocolat, fiche, shampoing
[d]	dimanche, code, addition
[f]	femme, dentifrice, chauffeur, bœuf, pharmacie, photographe
[g]	gare, légumes, goûter, guitare, langue, parking
[gz]	examen, exercice
[ʒ]	jeudi, déjeuner, âge, urgences
[k]	corps, placard, lecture, parc, quartier, équitation, cinq, basket, ticket
[ks]	sexe, saxophone, expliquer
[l]	lire, pantalon, collègue
[m]	mois, demain, immeuble,
[n]	nuage, avenue, anniversaire, automne
[ɲ]	montagne
[p]	parent, copain, appeler
[ʀ]	robe, courir, marron
[s]	soir, postal, piscine, naissance, ça, célibataire, place, merci, natation
[t]	table, batterie, théâtre
[v]	visiter, avion, avril
[z]	fraise, réserver, douze

Les chiffres et les nombres

0	zéro	**10**	dix
1	un	**11**	onze
2	deux	**12**	douze
3	trois	**13**	treize
4	quatre	**14**	quatorze
5	cinq	**15**	quinze
6	six	**16**	seize
7	sept	**17**	dix-sept
8	huit	**18**	dix-huit
9	neuf	**19**	dix-neuf

20, 21, 22, 23, 24, 25, 26, 27, 28, 29	**Vingt**, vingt-**et**-un, vingt-deux, vingt-trois, vingt-quatre, vingt-cinq, vingt-six, vingt-sept, vingt-huit, vingt-neuf
30, 31, 32, 33, 34, 35, 36, 37, 38, 39	**Trente**, trente-**et**-un, trente-deux, trente-trois, trente-quatre, trente-cinq, trente-six, trente-sept, trente-huit, trente-neuf
40, 41, 42, 43, 44, 45, 46, 47, 48, 49	**Quarante**, quarante-**et**-un, quarante-deux, quarante-trois, quarante-quatre, quarante-cinq, quarante-six, quarante-sept, quarante-huit, quarante-neuf
50, 51, 52, 53, 54, 55, 56, 57, 58, 59	**Cinquante**, cinquante-**et**-un, cinquante-deux, cinquante-trois, cinquante-quatre, cinquante-cinq, cinquante-six, cinquante-sept, cinquante-huit, cinquante-neuf
60, 61, 62, 63, 64, 65, 66, 67, 68, 69	**Soixante**, soixante-**et**-un, soixante-deux, soixante-trois, soixante-quatre, soixante-cinq, soixante-six, soixante-sept, soixante-huit, soixante-neuf
70, 71, 72, 73, 74, 75, 76, 77, 78, 79	**Soixante-dix**, soixante-**et**-onze, soixante-douze, soixante-treize, soixante-quatorze, soixante-quinze, soixante-seize, soixante-dix-sept, soixante-dix-huit, soixante-dix-neuf
80, 81, 82, 83, 84, 85, 86, 87, 88, 89	**Quatre-vingt**, quatre-vingt-un, quatre-vingt-deux, quatre-vingt-trois, quatre-vingt-quatre, quatre-vingt-cinq, quatre-vingt-six, quatre-vingt-sept, quatre-vingt-huit, quatre-vingt-neuf
90, 91, 92, 93, 94, 95, 96, 97, 98, 99	**Quatre-vingt-dix**, quatre-vingt-onze, quatre-vingt-douze, quatre-vingt-treize, quatre-vingt-quatorze, quatre-vingt-quinze, quatre-vingt-seize, quatre-vingt-dix-sept, quatre-vingt-dix-huit, quatre-vingt-dix-neuf

100	cent
1000	mille
10 000	dix mille
100 000	cent mille
1 000 000	un million
1 000 000 000	un milliard

Teach Yourself
Henna Tattoo

Teach Yourself
Henna Tattoo

Making Mehndi Art with Easy-to-Follow Instructions, Patterns, and Projects

BRENDA ABDOYAN

ACKNOWLEDGMENTS

To my husband, Anto, whom I love dearly
My daughter, Nic, and all the little chiclettes
My Mom, who is my hero, and my Dad, who has been hers
To all henna artisans who have been and still are the source of my inspiration, namely,
Catherine Cartwright-Jones of TapDancing Lizard LLC and TheHennaPage.com
And to all the friends, you know who you are, who painfully listened to me rave about
henna for years!

ISBN 978-1-57421-414-7

Library of Congress Cataloging-in-Publication Data

Abdoyan, Brenda.
Teach yourself henna tattoo / Brenda Abdoyan.
   p. cm.
Includes index.
ISBN 978-1-57421-414-7 (pbk.)
1. Mehndi (Body painting) 2. Temporary tattoos. I. Title.
GT2343.A23 2012
391.6--dc23
            2011032048

Printed in China
First printing

ABOUT THE AUTHOR

Brenda Abdoyan, a San Francisco-based child of the 1960s who considers everything to be art, is principal artist and designer at Bajidoo, Inc., a jewelry and design studio. Inspired by things from everyday life, she begins her creations with realism and then sprinkles them with the spice of life. Recently, she won top honors for the Designer Press Kit Award at a Craft and Hobby Association show.

She holds a degree in business administration and project management from the University of Phoenix. After more than 20 years as a senior business analyst in corporate America, she left it all to pursue her passion. Henna art was the road that took her home. Her first YouTube video on henna tattoo design led to her work being included in the March 2009 cable channel series *My Art* by Ovation Television. From there, she has expanded her henna canvas to include leather, wood, and bangles. Follow her at *www.bajidoo.com.*

CONTENTS

INTRODUCTION

A prudent question is one-half of wisdom. —
Francis Bacon

My henna saga began with a trip to the Middle East in 2000. Unlike the henna tattoo artist you may find on the beach in summer or in your favorite theme parks, henna artists in the Middle East apply tattoos behind the blacked-out windows of a beauty salon. The windows are blacked out to preserve the modesty of the ladies inside; the henna application is a complete experience.

A friend (the sister of the man who would later become my husband) and I entered the salon and were led up a dark, steep, narrow stairway. When we reentered the light at the top of stairs, we were in another world. Aromas assaulted us—cardamom spice in Arabic coffee (the essential oils used in henna paste) and burning incense.

The room, which comprised the entire upper floor, had no stations where a guest would sit in a specific chair for her henna application. Instead, the space was nearly empty in the center with banks of ornately decorated pillows along the sides. We simply sat on a mass of these overly soft pillows and the work began.

Since both my hands and feet were being done, four young girls worked through the designs, one on each hand and each foot. These four girls talked and giggled amongst themselves, only occasionally putting together a few words in English to ask me questions about my prior experience with henna tattoos (at that time, I had none). Something about those moments ignited a spark in me that continues to burn.

While the use of henna for tattoos is difficult to trace, evidence shows that it stretches back more than 5,000 years to the days of ancient Egypt when a henna dye was used to stain the fingers and toes of the pharaohs prior to their mummification. Henna tattooing has a long history among many Eastern cultures. The designs tend to fall into four styles based on the region. The Middle Eastern style in the Arab world features floral designs that do not follow a distinctive pattern. In North Africa, henna tattoos are geometrical and follow the shape of the wearer's hands and feet. In India and Pakistan, the designs cover more of the body, extending up arms and legs to give the impression of gloves or stockings. Henna tattoos in Indonesia and southern Asia are often blocks of color on the tips of the fingers and toes.

Many of the historical styles of henna tattoos remain popular today, but their use has grown to include Celtic designs, Chinese characters,

and American Indian symbols. Because of the temporary nature of henna tattoos, many people have begun experimenting with designs that express their individual styles and beliefs.

Culturally, the most common modern reference to henna tattooing is its use in traditional Hindu wedding ceremonies. Intricate designs, known as Mehndi, are applied to the bride's hands and feet to symbolize her commitment to her husband-to-be. Since the henna paste must remain on the skin for a couple of days, it restricts the movements and tasks of the bride. Its application gives her time to reflect on her upcoming marriage.

Henna is like many things: What you get out of it is directly proportional to what you put into it. While I started learning about henna in 2000, I only began to work with henna paste at the beginning of 2008. Yes, you read that right.

The first henna tattoo I made was on my right foot. I sat on my patio and drew on my foot.

I did a terrible job. I made the paste wrong; it was too thin. I had no coordination to create the images I had seen in books and online. I was completely frustrated. Even worse, after all my trouble, my ugly little tattoo image never even got dark! In no time at all I figured out that knowing the history and traditions of henna was fulfilling on one level, but tattoos wouldn't just spring forth from my hands because I had studied so diligently. To find fulfillment, I had to do more work in an entirely new direction.

This book is my way of helping you skip some or all of my frustration. I've included an extensive section on making henna paste and applying it (page 12). You will find information on the basic lines you'll need to master before creating beautiful tattoos. Don't skip this

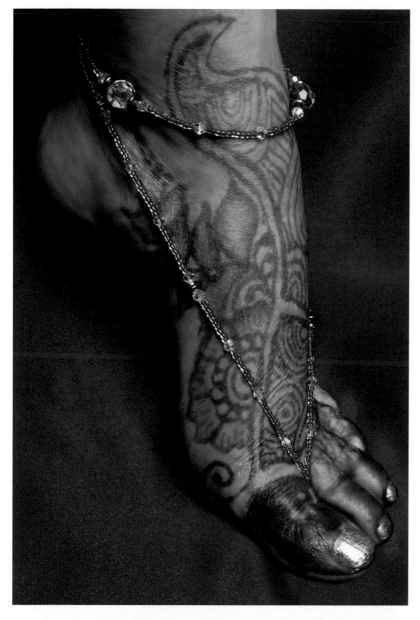

section! The better control you have in making the basic lines—which are the foundation of all henna tattoos—the better your finished tattoos will look.

The next section (page 26) focuses on applying henna tattoos to the body. Work through the projects to develop your henna tattooing skills. There are tons of gallery photos here to inspire you.

The next section is filled with designs for use on hands, feet, lower back, and shoulders (page 46). As you become more familiar with henna tattoos, you will be able to adapt these designs. I've also included the templates I use to develop new designs. Just follow the shape of the hand or foot to create your own unique henna tattoos.

Finally, the stain left behind from the application of henna paste is not just ideal for skin, but it also works well on other mediums, including wood and leather. Henna designs applied to the latter may fade a bit, but they won't wear off like the henna tattoos applied to your skin! Check out some of my ideas for henna on objects on page 98.

If you try henna tattooing and have difficulty, snap a picture and email it to me at info@bajidoo.com. I will respond as quickly as I am able with some suggestions.

A random event on a short holiday was the spark that quickly caused a firestorm of creativity deep in my heart. From the first instant that henna entered my life, it was kismet. I hope this book provides a similar spark of passion in you. So let's get started making the paste and creating beautiful henna tattoos.

Regards,
Brenda Abdoyan, Bajidoo, Inc.

SETTING UP

The first step in mastering the art of henna tattoos is to make sure you have the right materials on hand. The items you'll need to create your own henna tattoos are not costly, but you'll want to have everything readily available before you get started. After that, it's practice, practice, practice!

MAKING HENNA PASTE

Before you do anything else you must first make or buy henna paste.

Henna paste is made by mixing a liquid with the powder from the dried, crushed leaves of a bush, *Lawsonia inermis*, which grows in the dry, hot regions of the Middle East. When applied to the skin, the greenish paste leaves behind an orange-red stain. This stain is only temporary and will wear away as the skin exfoliates over the next three to four weeks.

Henna paste is easy to make on your own, or you can purchase it from arts and craft supply stores (see Resources at the back of this book). If you buy premade henna paste, be sure to check the expiration date. It should be clearly marked on the package.

I prefer to make my own henna paste. The process of making the paste by hand is just one small part of the whole henna experience.

HOMEMADE HENNA PASTE

If you choose to make your own henna paste, you will need a recipe. I started experimenting with my henna recipe in 2005 and perfected it through trial and error in 2008. I suggest you start your trials with my recipe and then alter it if you need to. You'll find notes in the ingredient list below that will help you determine what to change.

My current recipe for henna paste has turned out perfectly every time for me, but when I first began to make henna paste, I goofed it up a lot, so give yourself space for making mistakes.

TIP A good test for the correct consistency is to take ¼ tsp. of the paste and drop it on a plate. It should stand up from the surface of the plate and retain much of its form, similar to the way frosting on a cake retains its shape from the strokes of the spatula blade.

Above all be patient with yourself. All good things take some amount of time to perfect.

Let's gather up the ingredients you'll need and get started on the paste! In the back of this book I have included some Web sites and other suggestions for where to get the ingredients in the list.

Henna powder is made from the leaves of a bush that grows in the dry Middle Eastern regions.

To make henna paste you'll need to mix the powder with acidic liquids like lemon juice and with essential oils both from seeds and distilled sources.

RECIPE: HENNA PASTE

- 6 oz. (177 ml) brewed coffee, black
- 1 Tbsp. (15 g) each of peppercorns, whole cloves, and whole cumin seeds, mixed together
- 2 cinnamon sticks
- 1.75 oz. (50 g) henna powder
- Juice of 1 lemon, or about 2 tbsp. (90 ml) reconstituted juice
- 2 tsp. (10 g) granulated sugar
- 2 tsp. (30 ml) tea tree oil

TIP Not quite ready to tattoo yet but have already mixed your paste? Simply keep it in the zipper-top plastic bag and pop it in the freezer. It will keep there for two to three months. Thaw it at room temperature when you're ready to tattoo.

1. Brew 6 oz. of strong black coffee.

2. Drop a good-sized handful of peppercorns, whole cloves, and whole cumin seeds plus a couple cinnamon sticks into a hot cup of black coffee. Let it steep for 3 to 4 minutes.

3. In a 2- to 3-cup (.5 to .75 l) plastic container with a lid, put about 1.75 oz. (50 g) of henna powder (half a box of Jamila if you chose this brand).

4. Pour the coffee mixture, a little at a time, through a strainer into the henna powder, mixing the liquid in at each interval until the mixture resembles mashed potatoes.

5. Squeeze the juice of 1 lemon through the strainer into the henna paste.

6. Add sugar, and mix well. Let the mixture stand covered at 70°F to 90°F for about 10 to 20 hours. After it has rested, the paste should look very dark green and the surface of the paste will have a light sheen.

7. Add tea tree oil, and stir. The paste should be similar in thickness to cake frosting, whipped butter, or toothpaste. Adjust the consistency if necessary by adding more lemon juice.

8. Spoon the paste into a zipper-top bag to let it rest 72 hours at 70°F to 90°F. Store the paste in the plastic bag until it is time to tattoo. If the tattooing will not occur within the next several days, freeze the paste in the bag and thaw it when you're ready to begin tattooing. Premixed paste will keep for 2 to 3 months in the freezer.

The henna powder (left) turns into a paste (right) that will stain the skin temporarily.

HENNA PASTE NECESSITIES

Henna powder. Be sure to get fresh powder; the year of the crop should be listed on the box or bag. Make sure that the packaging does not mention "hair dye." Henna on its own can add shine to natural hair, but henna that is used for hair coloring often includes dyes that are harmful to the skin and can result in allergic reactions and even burns. I often mix two brands of henna powder together in one recipe.

Coffee. You can use any type of coffee derived from the coffee bean—from instant to French press—as long as you brew it strong and hot, but not boiling. Contrary to popular belief, the coffee doesn't add color to the paste; however, the acid in the coffee helps to pull the color out of the crushed henna leaves. Don't have coffee on hand? A strong, dark, black tea will provide the same effect.

Lemon juice. Just like coffee, lemon juice adds acid, and acid breaks down the cellular structure of the henna powder to bring out the color. Either squeeze the juice from one lemon or use an equal amount of reconstituted lemon juice. I've also heard of other acidic ingredients being substituted for lemon juice. Apple cider vinegar is one option, but the smell would be quite strong and likely unpleasant compared to lemon!

> **TIP** To test if your henna is ready to use for tattooing, place the zipper-top plastic bag on a white paper towel or plain sheet of white tablet paper and wait approximately 15 to 20 minutes. Lift the bag at the end of the time period. The paper should have a light orange shadow where the bag was sitting. Bingo, you're ready to go!

Peppercorns, whole cloves, cinnamon sticks, whole cumin seeds. Yes, they smell good, but it's not the smell we're after in a henna paste recipe. Seeds of any kind contain essential oils that act as an accelerator and give the henna powder an extra punch, making it just a little darker than it would be on its own. If you're making your own recipe, feel free to try the seeds from any plant, but make sure that you or your tattooee isn't allergic.

Tea tree oil. Another essential oil, this one is added directly to the paste for consistency as well as acceleration. If you can't find tea tree oil, substitute eucalyptus oil. If the rather strong smell of either of those oils doesn't appeal to you, try adding some lemon or lavender oil to the tea tree oil. Remember to check on allergies to essential oils before application.

White sugar. Sugar adds the stickiness that the henna paste needs to stay on the skin long enough to leave a nice stain behind. You can use any kind of sugar, or you can try honey instead.

Strainer. Use the strainer to remove the seeds from the coffee and any pulp or seeds from the lemon juice. Any solid objects in the finished paste may clog your applicator and cause your lines to have skips or blobs.

Sandwich-sized plastic bag with a zipper top. After the henna paste is mixed it needs to rest. A small bag with a secure closure will keep air from getting to the paste and making it hard.

It only takes about 10 minutes to make henna paste, but it is not ready to use for tattoos until it has rested at a temperature of 72°F to 80°F for at least 72 hours. Be sure to figure in this extra time when setting a time to do your tattoos. You'll need to make the paste at least three days before you want to start tattooing!

TRIAL AND ERROR

While trial and error are great ways to discover the ultimate henna paste recipe, not everyone has the several years I took to perfect a recipe. Here are some things I've learned to put you one step—or maybe two or three—ahead of the trial and error curve.

- You *can't* change the color that's left behind by natural henna paste. I've known people to try beet juice—which by itself will stain your hands red in a heartbeat—instead of coffee, but they ended up with the same orange-red color.

- You can make the stain from natural henna paste slightly darker by changing the types of essential oils (they come from the seeds) you use in your recipe or by wiping the area to be tattooed with a bit of tea tree or eucalyptus oil before applying the paste.

- If you really don't like the orange-red color of henna tattoos, you can try another natural temporary tattoo substance made from the pulp of the jagua fruit. Employed by native South American tribes, this gel leaves behind a dark blue-black stain. The mixture can be applied through a Mylar henna cone and leaves a tattoo that will last for seven to nine days.

- Try mixing two or more brands of henna powder in your recipe. You may find that the unique qualities of each growing region produce a more or less potent powder, giving your resulting tattoo a darker or lighter shade. I've tried Jamila and Henna from Yemen with good results.

- It's always good to sift henna powder right out of the bag before you mix it into your recipe, but that step is extremely important if you're planning to apply a tattoo that has intricate details. One piece of leaf or stem can jam your applicator, causing you to alter your design.

- Avoid making paste that is too thin; it will run and the definition of your tattoo will be lost. As an insurance policy, set aside 1 to 2 rounded tablespoons of sifted henna powder. If you make the henna paste too thin, simply add the extra powder back in to thicken the paste.

- Always add your liquid—coffee, lemon juice, oil—in small amounts. Think of the stated amounts in the recipe as guidelines. Getting the correct consistency of the final paste is more important than adding in the precise amounts of each ingredient. You want "mashed potatoes" after the first stage and "frosting" after the second stage.

- Whole seeds generally have more essential oils, but ground spices will have some as well. Use what you have on hand. Ground cinnamon, ground cloves, and ground pepper, for example, can be substituted for their whole counterparts.

CAUTION:
- Make sure that the henna powder packaging does not mention "hair dye." Henna on its own can add shine to natural hair, but henna that is used for hair coloring often includes dyes and chemicals that are harmful to the skin and can result in allergic reactions or even burns.

- Be aware of allergies to essential oils and always research the essential oils you use. Undiluted essential oils are not safe to use directly on human skin, and some can have adverse effects for pregnant women and small children.

APPLYING HENNA PASTE

Henna paste can be applied to skin as tattoos or to other natural, porous surfaces (untreated wood, tambourine and drum heads, or leather, for example) as decoration.

SKIN

If you decide to work on skin, prepare the surface by swabbing it with alcohol. The alcohol will kill any germs on the surface of the skin and keep other germs from being transferred during the tattooing process.

Some people may choose to prepare the area by rubbing it with tea tree oil, eucalyptus oil, or any other essential oil mixed with some carrier oil. While these oils are a part of the natural henna paste recipe, the extra application directly to the skin may help to make the final tattoo just a bit darker.

Note: This preparation method will not kill germs and other bacteria.

Another consideration before applying henna paste to skin is to make sure the area is free of open wounds or recently healed scratches. The skin is your body's largest organ; be careful to avoid harming it in any way. Always, always, always do a test patch first to see how your body will react to the paste. The inner elbow is a good spot.

If you're not quite ready to freehand henna paste directly to the skin, you can use a brown-toned watercolor pencil to sketch out the design on your skin first. The pencil marks are removable if you don't like what you draw, and they can't be seen under the henna if you decide to apply the paste directly on top of the marks.

Henna paste can be removed after as little as two hours to reveal the orange-burgundy temporary tattoo left behind (left). Leaving the paste on longer, however, is always better.

TIP When it comes to henna tattoos, inquiry as to whether your subject is pregnant is not an invasion of privacy; it's a necessary safety measure. Some essential oils used in henna paste or as a preparation directly on the skin's surface can be harmful to pregnant women. Rosemary oil, for example, can send a woman into early labor. Always ask first!

Use a piece of graphite paper to trace over an image in order to transfer it to an object.

OBJECTS

Because of the nature of henna paste, it will leave behind its signature orange-red stain on any natural, porous surface. Untreated wood is ideal. This wood must be completely natural—do not finish it with *any* substance, from chemical finishes, like varnish, to natural finishes, like linseed oil.

Leather is another surface that takes henna designs very well. You can decorate drum heads or tambourine skins, as well as lamp shades and other objects made out of untreated animal skins.

Again, if you're not quite ready to freehand a design directly on an object, try transferring it first by going over a copy of the tattoo with a graphite pencil. Press as lightly as possible to transfer the graphite to the surface; if your graphite goes on too dark you will see it later when the henna paste is removed.

CHOOSE AN APPLICATION TOOL

There are several ways to apply henna to a surface to create a tattoo design. Try each of the methods listed below until you find the one that is most comfortable for you.

Soft plastic squeeze bottle. Any type of small squeeze bottle that fits comfortably into your hand is ideal. Jacquard Products makes a variety of these types of bottles. Look for 1 ounce (30 ml) bottles. Anything larger will be hard to handle and anything smaller will be too stiff to squeeze.

Mylar cone. This method of applying henna paste is most popular, and it is the method I use throughout the book. Look for the how-to instructions on making your own Mylar cones in this chapter (page 20).

Syringe. Any type of syringe will work. Be sure to clip off the sharp tip and file the needle to a dull finish so it will not perforate the skin.

Paintbrush. Use a paintbrush to apply a wash of 1 part water and 1 part henna paste to an area you have mapped out prior to tattooing or within an outline of a tattoo for a two-toned effect. Choose a brush with bristles made from flexible natural fibers.

ROLL-YOUR-OWN HENNA CONE

Just like henna paste, applicators made from Mylar (a transparent gift wrap often used to wrap fresh-cut flowers) can be handmade or purchased. I'll give you instructions here to make your own, or you can purchase them premade through one of the suppliers listed in the back of the book (see Resources on page 110). Whichever method you choose, be sure to make or purchase two or three so you can quickly and efficiently apply lines of different widths.

To make a Mylar cone by hand, begin by cutting a 10" x 8" rectangular portion of Mylar (see right). Now cut the rectangle in two, from the longest point to opposite longest point. You will end up with two right triangles.

Place the triangle in front of you on a smooth, dry surface. Position the triangle so the long side is on the left if you're right handed, and on the right if you're left handed.

Locate the midway point along the longest side. Place your first digit (pointing finger) on that spot. From the shorter pointy side of the triangle, lift the bottom corner up and curl it over your finger to create a cone shape.

Using your thumb and first digit, guide the tip of the cone so that it keeps its shape—do not pinch or put pressure on the tip. Just keep it between your fingers so it remains tight in form. Continue rolling the cone from the other side until the triangle is completely rolled onto

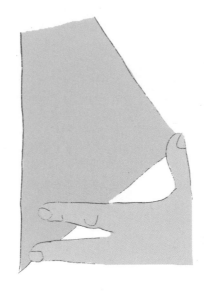

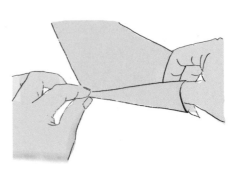

Cut a 10" x 8" (255 x 205mm) piece of Mylar into two triangles.

Lightly pinch the long side of the triangle at the midpoint. Start to roll the cone from the pointed side of the triangle.

The resulting cones should be tightly closed at the point.

itself. When you're finished, it will resemble an ice cream cone; the tip will be completely closed. Tape the cone closed along the open side, leaving the top open.

Now you're ready to fill the cone about two-thirds full of henna paste. Clip the lower corner off one side of the zipper-top bag and squeeze the paste into your applicator. Do not overfill the cone. Overfull cones make a big mess when you try to use them.

> **TIP** You need only about 50 grams (1.75 oz.) of henna powder to make enough paste for two hands, top and bottom, and the tops of both feet. And when mixed, that 50 grams (1.75 oz.) of dry powder will make just about the right amount to fill two standard "roll-your-own" applicator cones. You could make one super cone to hold all the paste, but I always make two: I clip one for a fine tip and the other for a bold or thicker line.

Use a nail clipper to clip the end of the cone. Removing this much of the Mylar will create a fairly thick line. Remove about half this much for a thinner line.

The results of a two different cuts at the tip of the cone. A smaller cut gives a thinner line, as shown on the top example.

CLIPPING THE CONE

Once you have made and filled your cones, you'll have to clip the tip of the cone so the paste can flow freely. I always have several cones on hand with various sizes of openings at the tips. Having options at my fingertips makes the tattoo application go much faster and allows me to be more creative on the spur of the moment.

For a fine line, just whisper the end of the cone off with the clippers. Try the cone out on a piece of paper. If you clipped too much to get the kind of detail you're hoping for, use this cone to shade larger areas or create a thick outline or border for your designs. Then clip another cone by taking off a smaller amount than you removed from the first one.

HENNA PASTE REMOVAL

The simplest way to remove the henna paste after the appropriate amount of time has passed (as little as 2 to 4 hours, but 12 to 24 hours if possible) is to just let it crumble up and fall off on its own like an autumn leaf falls from a tree in due time. But this is not the tidiest method. Like the leaves on a tree, the paste does not all fall off at the same moment in time. A method that is much cleaner and easier to tolerate is the "craft glue method" of paste removal.

HENNA TATTOO TIMELINE

Henna tattoos—from preparing the paste to allowing the paste to dry—take time. Plan ahead for the best results.

Day 1: Make the paste and allow it to rest.

Day 4: Place the bag on a white piece of paper. If the bag leaves a shadow after 15 to 20 minutes, it's time to apply the paste.

Day 4: Apply the paste. Allow it to remain on the skin for at least 2 hours. Longer is always better. Don't wash the tattooed area for at least 24 hours. For objects, allow the paste to dry for 3 to 5 days.

TIP Want to give your henna tattoo a little more dimension? Make a wash of half water and half henna paste, then apply it to the skin prior to applying the tattoo. The lighter stain of the wash will give the tattoo a two-toned effect. You can also outline the tattoo first then use a wet brush to pull color to the inner area of the tattoo for a watercolor effect.

THE CRAFT GLUE METHOD OF REMOVAL

While I am certain there are as many suggested ways to remove henna paste as there are techniques for applying it, I have found that the craft glue method is the single most tidy and tolerable technique to do so. All you need is a bit of children's non-toxic, hypo-allergenic water-based craft glue found in most local craft stores. Place equal portions of the glue and clear tap water in a small container or bowl. Mix the two ingredients well; it will be quite thin.

After you have applied the henna paste and it has set up to the point where it is no longer shiny and will not easily move when touched, carefully brush the glue wash over the entire tattoo with a soft bristle brush. It is important that some moisture is still present in the paste. You can add some glitter to the glue wash before you apply it to add a little sparkle to your tattoo; the glue will dry clear.

Allow the glue wash to dry, and leave it on until the wash begins to lift off on its own at the edges (about 2 to 4 hours). At this point you can peel up the glue wash and remove it very much like a bandage (without the ouch factor of bandage adhesive!). The best part of the craft glue method of henna paste removal is that the glue lifts off easily, taking all the henna paste along with it in one clean continuous motion. Just toss the refuse away—no mess, no fuss.

The stain left behind by the henna paste will continue to darken over time. This photo shows the depth of the stain at 24 hours after paste removal.

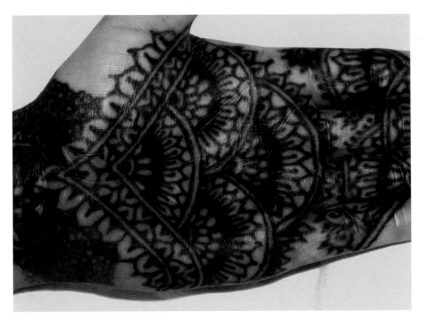

This photo shows the depth of the stain at 72 hours after paste removal.

TIP Always work in tiny increments—smaller than you think necessary—when you're clipping the tip of your cone. You can always clip again, but you can't put it back if you cut too much. If you mess up, simply squeeze the contents of the unusable cone into the new one. No reason to toss out the henna paste with the bad cone!

PRACTICE

The great thing about henna tattoos is that even a very simple design can look intricate and complex when complete. Take, for instance, the common flower. You will see flowers used in henna tattoo designs all the time. Almost all flowers begin with the same stroke: a simple circle. The tricky thing about applying henna paste is not the artistic aspect as much as it is retraining the muscles in your hands to do something they likely have not done before.

Applying henna paste looks as if it should be very easy—after all, you're holding the cone very much like a pen. It should be like doodling at the very least, right? Unfortunately, it isn't. The cone requires more hand-eye coordination because you have to know when and how much pressure to apply while you're making the artistic sweeping motions of the tattoo. The best way to get your hand familiar with the process is to practice.

HENNA TATTOO SHAPES

Five base figures make up the more common elements of Mehndi-inspired henna tattoo designs:

- Circle
- Petal
- Leaf, or Spire
- Curlicue, or Question Mark
- Straight Line

The best way to practice is on a piece of paper. Let's start with the circle.

First, draw a basic circle on a piece of paper with a pen and clip your cone to a fine point (see Clipping the Cone on page 21). Then, using the henna cone, make the same circle over and over again on the paper. You will soon become comfortable with the henna cone and the amount of pressure to apply. This repetition is how you train the muscles in your hand to do what you want.

Practice each of the five strokes on a piece of paper until you can make them consistently. If you master these strokes individually, you will do just fine making some very beautiful henna tattoos.

Enough reading, right? Are you making those shapes in good, consistent fashion? Then let's get going on the tattoo practice part.

THE BASIC FLOWER

Look closely at this basic henna flower tattoo. The five strokes you just practiced are used to make this common pattern.

Most henna tattoos begin with some variation of these five strokes. Your tattoo designs are only limited by your imagination and how you put the strokes together to create beautiful images.

It's a bit of a curiosity, but for some reason to create artistic balance in the completed design, you should use odd numbers of objects. That is to say, one flower or three for a group, rather than two or four.

> **TIP** Working with a henna cone to create tattoos is very similar, in my mind, to the art of cake decorating. With practice, your hand will soon respond to your desire to create specific shapes using this new tool. It may seem boring, but practicing the basic shapes until the muscles in your hand become trained is essential.

HENNA TATTOO SHAPES WORKSHEET

Make a copy of this page and practice using henna over the shapes.
You'll be confident in your abilities to freehand the designs in no time!

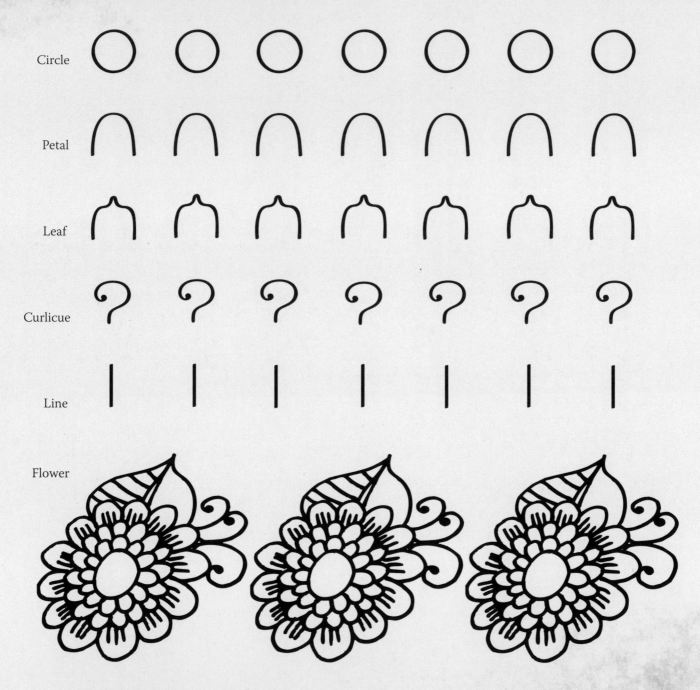

Circle

Petal

Leaf

Curlicue

Line

Flower

Put all five of the basic shapes together with
the flower design.

PRACTICING THE BASIC FLOWER

1

Start the flower with the circle.

2

Continue by making repeated petals (upside down U shapes) all around the circle.

3

Add a single dot inside each petal for further definition, then start on the larger version of the U-shaped petals.

4

Add a few straight lines inside the bigger petals. Like the dot in the smaller petals, this line adds definition and complexity to the final design.

5

Next add a leaf. Inside the leaf add the straight lines. To finish, add a small grouping of curlicues.

6

You could stop there and have a perfectly beautiful tattoo design. Or you could add another flower by repeating the same steps over again.

HENNA BODY TATTOOS

Human skin makes an ideal canvas for henna tattoos. Because of the nature of henna paste, the resulting dye does not leave a permanent mark on the skin, allowing you to try various designs based on your own whims or according to special events you have planned for that month. Let's get started with your first tattoo, a classic flower that incorporates all the basic lines you learned; then, we'll move on to the more intricate tattoo designs for your hands.

Your First Tattoo

{ **SKILL LEVEL:** ❀ BEGINNER

Let's go to the palm of your hand for your first tattoo. Why the palm? Simply because it is close. You can see what you're doing without contorting your arm or leg, and you can still protect your work somewhat from public view by simply keeping the palm of your hand to yourself.

TIP Don't want *anyone* to see your first attempt at tattooing yourself? Instead of working on the palm of your hand, work on the soles of your feet. They are invisible to others, making them the best place to practice your new skill—although they may be a little hard to reach.

Use the same flower image that you practiced earlier (see The Basic Flower on page 25). It is always a good idea, especially when you are just starting out, to practice drawing the tattoo on paper first with the henna paste and cone.

For your first—or every—tattoo, here's a trick you can use to get a perfect pattern on the skin before you place the henna. Go to your local craft store and purchase a brown-toned watercolor pencil. Dip the pencil in water and draw your design on your skin before you tattoo. If you don't like what you see, simply wipe off the pencil marks and try again. When you have the image the way you want it, tattoo right over the drawn sketch.

Mistakes with the henna cone are bound to happen. If you make a mistake, use a damp cotton swab or tip of a toothpick to remove the stray henna. If you want to wipe off the henna and start over, use alcohol wipes from the drug store or a cotton ball moistened with alcohol. The alcohol evaporates fast and seems to retard the henna stain development.

Begin with a circle. Here you can see the watercolor pencil I used to draw the original design on my palm. Begin with the circle stroke, move on to the petal shape, and finish with the leaf, following the lines with the henna cone.

Allow the paste to remain. When complete, let the henna dry, remaining on your hand for a minimum of two hours. Longer is always better.

Finger Tattoo

SKILL LEVEL: ❀ INTERMEDIATE

Our second tattoo design looks more complex, but as you can see from the highlighted area in the photos, the same common strokes from the basic henna flower are used here. However, instead of showing the full flower, we will draw only half the design—as if the rest is hidden behind the gently curving line that extends from wrist to finger tip—and repeat it along the length of the curvy line.

TIP Try not to wash the tattooed area for 24 hours after the paste has been removed. For tattoos on the hands this can be tricky when you live an active life! But if you can manage it, the tattoo will last longer. One idea that works for me: do the tattoo right before bed.

If you are not comfortable with freehanding the henna paste directly on the skin, practice on paper first or draw guidelines on the skin with a brown-toned watercolor pencil. This design is labeled as intermediate skill level because of the need to keep the paste flowing smoothly from the tube for the entire length of the wrist and hand.

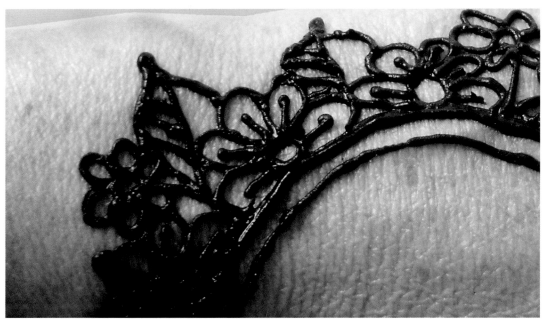

The complexity is somewhat of an illusion. Notice how this design is made up of the same five basic lines used in Project 1.

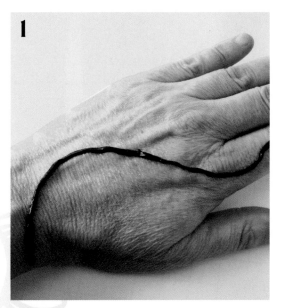

Start near the wrist. I started at the base of the line near my wrist and worked my way up the curve.

Repeat the design. Repetitive simple flowers form a cluster design, turning simple individual objects into a much more complex tattoo once completed.

LACE GLOVE

{ **SKILL LEVEL:**  ADVANCED

For our last tattoo project, let's try something more intricate. Again, if you look closely at the design, you'll see that the lacey look of this tattoo was created with a series of simple repeated shapes, much like our first tattoo. This project is advanced because it requires more control to make the many evenly spaced lines and curves. As always, warm up by practicing on a piece of paper first.

TIP Henna tattoos need a humid environment to "take." A recipe that works perfectly in steamy Florida might not react so well for someone in the drier regions of Arizona. Try adding more sugar or honey to encourage the paste to stay in place longer, or wrap the tattooed appendage in plastic wrap when the henna is dry.

Try to work in a natural progression down the length of your hand. It is important that the lines remain as consistent as possible. Inconsistent lines will result in a tattoo with lines that are not sharply defined, which will make the tattoo look a bit sloppy.

Allow the henna paste to stay in place for a minimum of two to four hours, or 12 to 24 hours if possible, then remove it (see page 21). Bravo! Your delicate henna lace glove is ready to be shown off to the world.

1. Begin at the peak of the lines above the wrist. Start with the double lines above the wrist. Note that the line closer to my fingers is made with a thicker applicator cone. Start to add the half moon shapes, petals, and dots that form the portion of the design at the point of the lines.

2. Continue adding scale-shaped areas to fill in. Make a double line to separate one portion of the design from the next, then continue on. The top part of this design is created by linking together three sections of the same repeating pattern.

3. Draw a large pointed teardrop shape on the back of the hand. Open up the central part of the design by outlining a pointed teardrop shape on the back of the hand. Because the final bit of the design spills down the middle finger, you'll want to make sure that the point of the teardrop is in line with the center of the middle finger. Add a few simple curves and circles inside the space you created.

4. Expand the edges of the design with repeating patterns. Working from the top down to the point, add as many rows of half circles or other repeating design elements as you need to fill the area between the end of the pointed teardrop and the knuckle of the middle finger.

TIP To keep the dried henna paste on your hand longer, mix equal portions of white craft glue (like Elmer's) and water, toss in some glister for a pretty distraction, then brush over the dried paste with a delicate stroke of a paintbrush. Best of all, when you peel away the dried glue, the henna paste comes off clean along with it. No scraping!

5. Add the final decoration down the center of the middle finger. Draw a central line down the middle finger and add leaves, petals, dots, and lines to complete the tattoo.

GALLERY

Using henna to create tattoos on human skin is a unique way to express your individuality in a not-so-permanent fashion. On the pages that follow, you'll find a number of examples of henna tattoos. Many of these designs follow Mehndi traditions, but you can use henna paste to draw geometric patterns, realistic objects, or lettering. Enjoy exploring your creativity with henna.

A geometric design that extends from the wrist to the tip of the first finger is balanced with softer curves that cover the palm of the hand.

A dense flower center is surrounded by leaves on the palm of the hand. The shiny look is from the craft glue wash that was applied to keep the henna paste in place longer.

A design that starts on the top of the hand continues to the palm.

A henna wash made with half water and half henna paste gives dimension to some of the open areas of this design.

Zigzag lines draw attention to the dense central part of this henna tattoo. Colored paint gives the tattoo a little extra interest as the henna paste dries.

The strength of the stain varies depending how long it was left on. The darker areas of this tattoo were applied first.

Designs do not have to be symmetrical and are often done freehand to complement the natural shape of the body.

Large shaded flower petals with starkly lined leaves form a unique design for the palm of the hand.

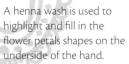
A henna wash is used to highlight and fill in the flower petals shapes on the underside of the hand.

Designs extend across the closed fingers of the underside of the hand so that the areas between the fingers are left blank.

Leaf shapes extend from a central flower following the line of the fingers. Note that the henna design does not go between the fingers.

Once the henna paste is removed, a dark orange-burgundy stain is left in its place. The stain will continue to darken for about 72 hours. This photo was taken 24 hours after application.

Henna tattoos look best when designed to fit the profile of the area being tattooed. This lily flower rests above the knee where it is easily visible when sitting or standing, while the leaves wrap below the kneecap.

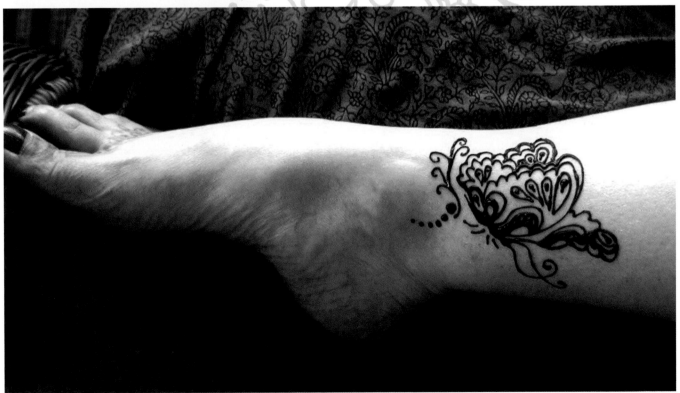

Small henna tattoo designs at the ankle can be reminiscent of ink tattoos.

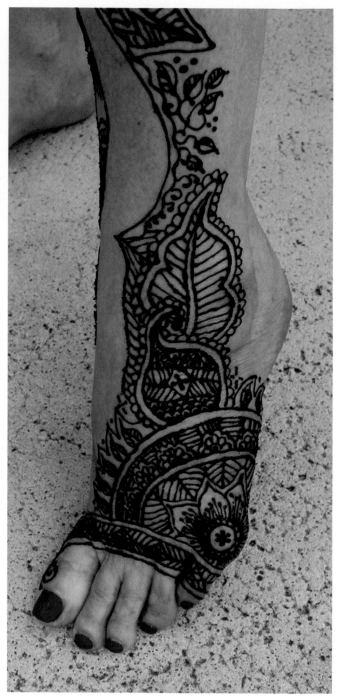

Remember the curlicue—one of the five basic shapes? It really takes center stage in this design. I also like the wispy look added by the chains of dots.

Henna tattoos can easily be extended from the tips of the toes along the calf.

Henna paste can be removed after as little as two hours to reveal the orange-burgundy temporary tattoo left behind (left). Leaving the paste on longer, however, is always better.

This tattoo was designed to echo the shape of the heel and the calf as it reaches up the leg.

Designs and Templates

As with new skills, the more you practice, the better you'll get. Here are a few original Bajidoo designs for you to try on as your talent grows. Some of the designs are simple, in the sense that they are made up of only the five strokes we covered in the beginning of this book. Some are more complicated, so when you are ready to venture on you have a design to refer to. I've also included a handful of templates for your designing enjoyment. Good luck and happy tattooing!

HANDS

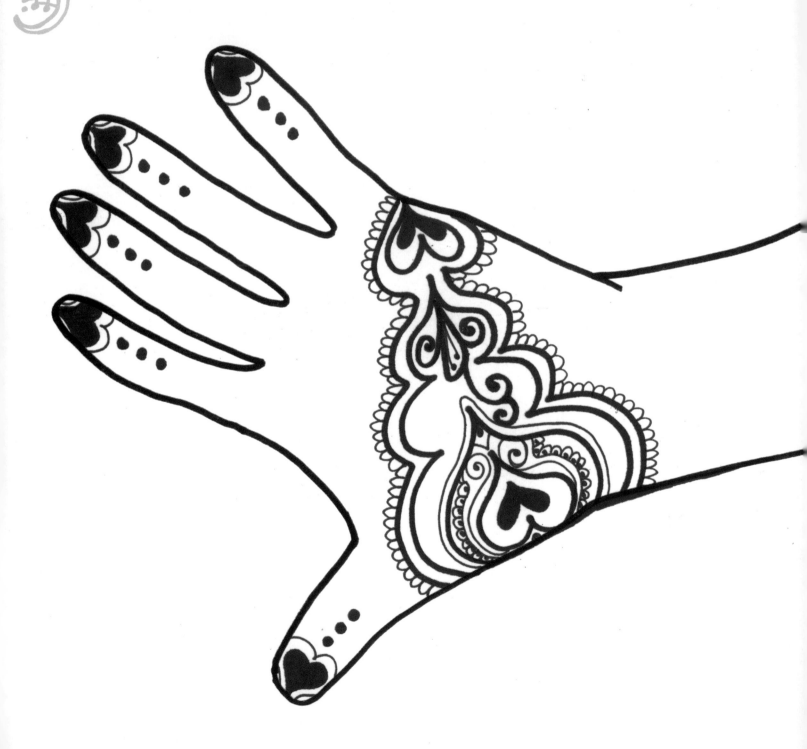

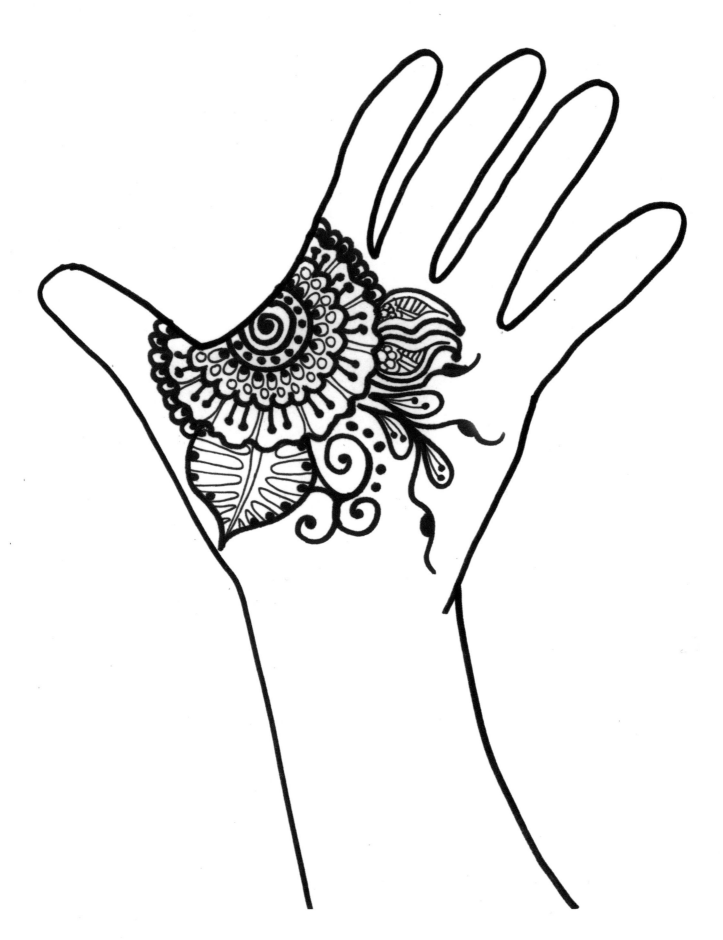

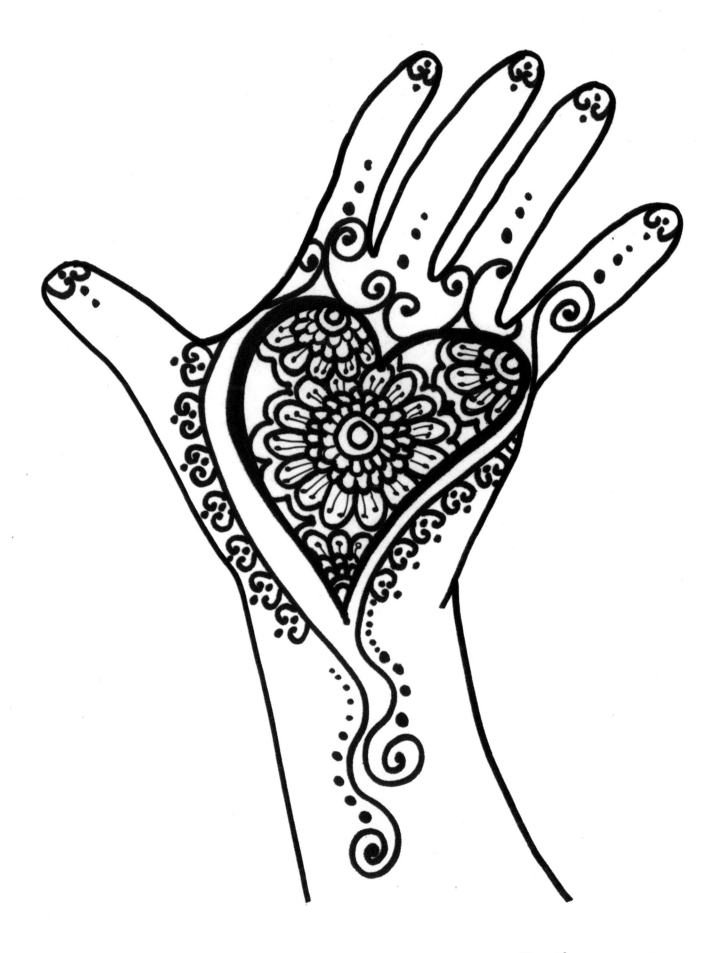

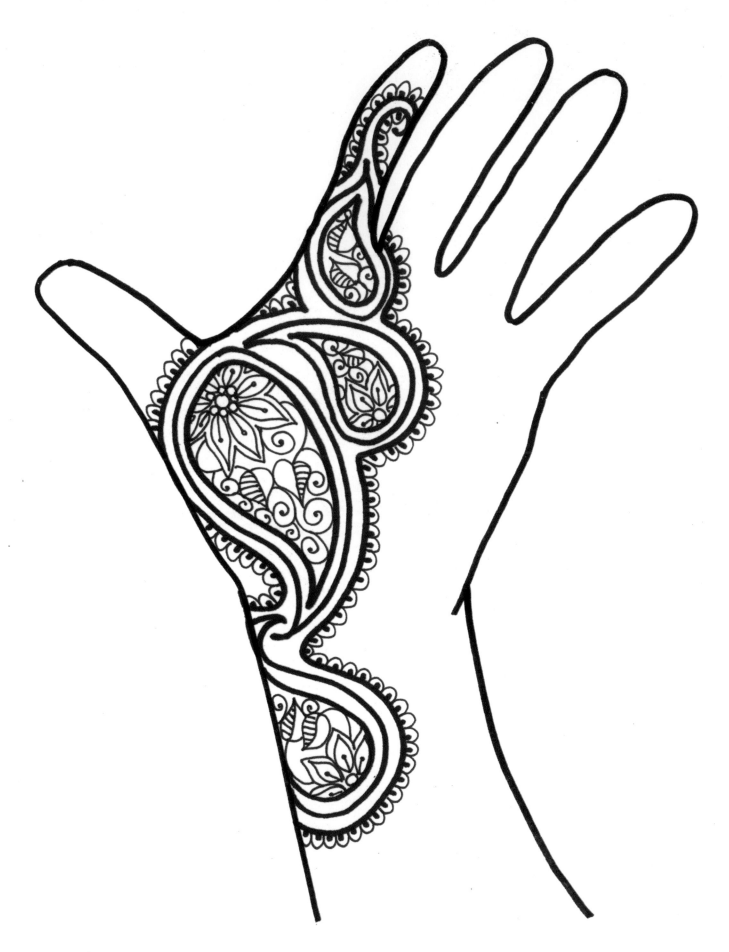

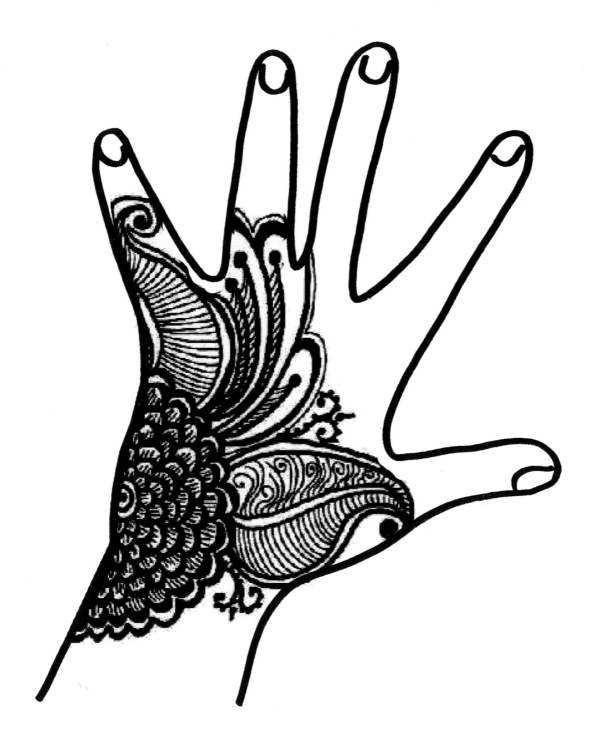

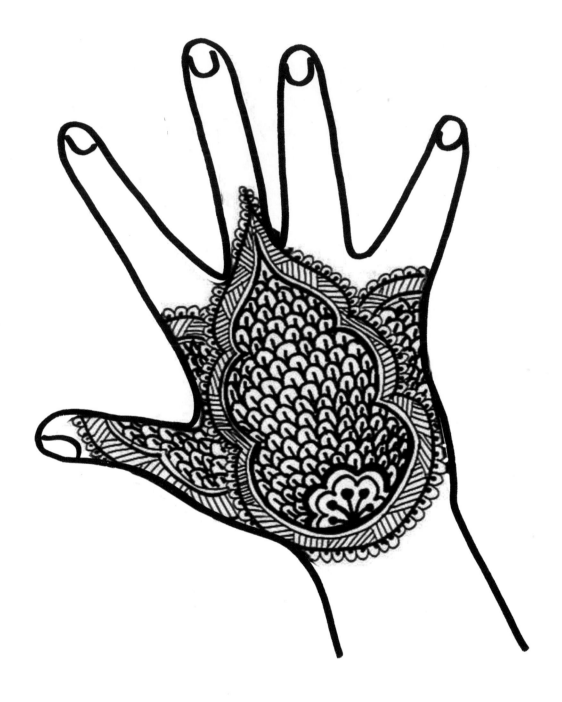

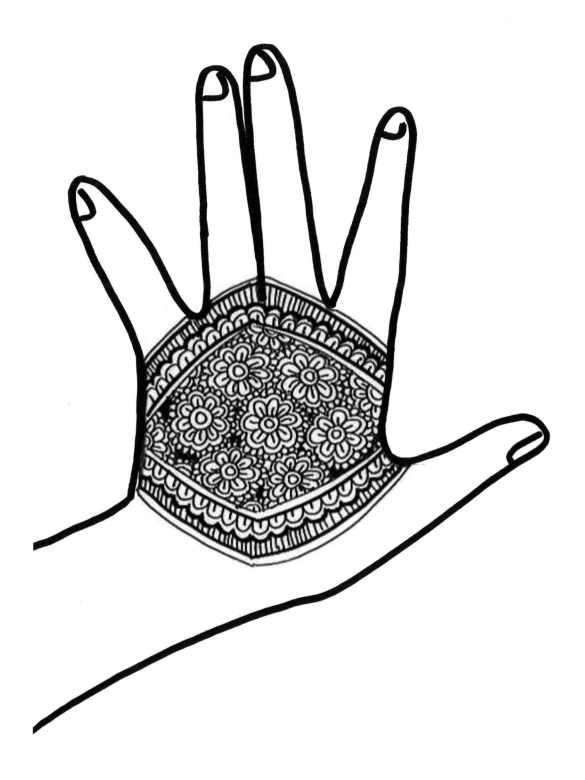

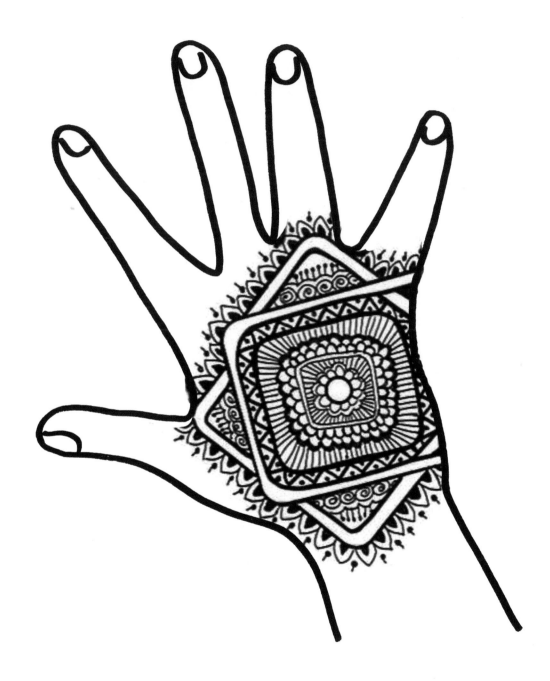

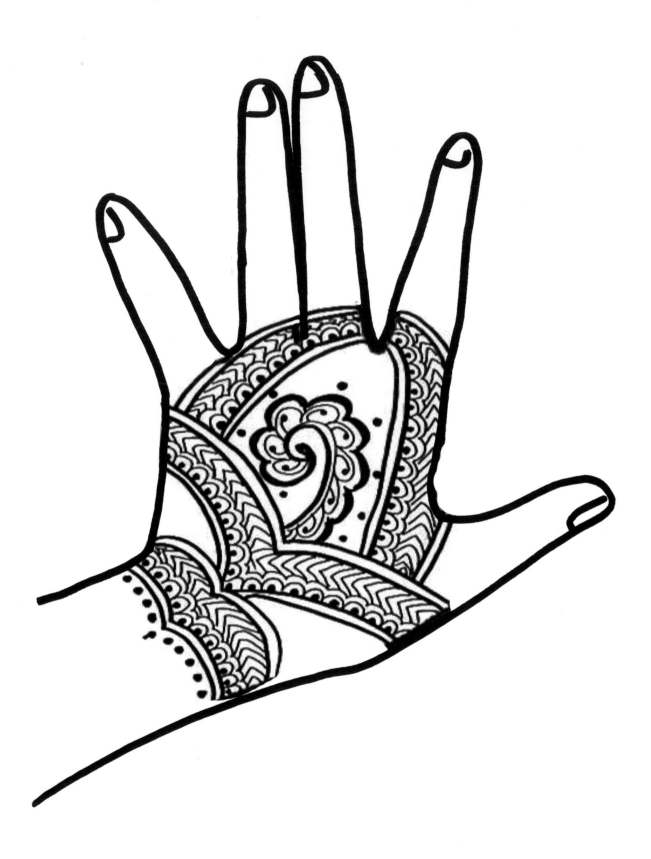

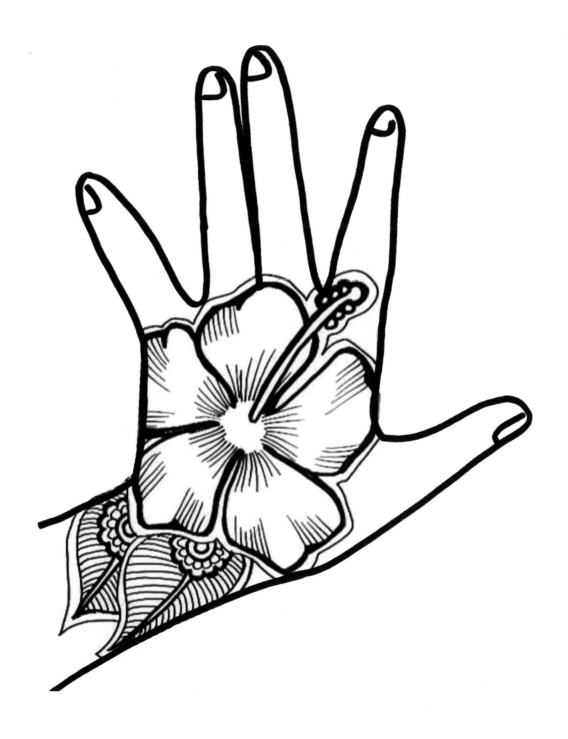

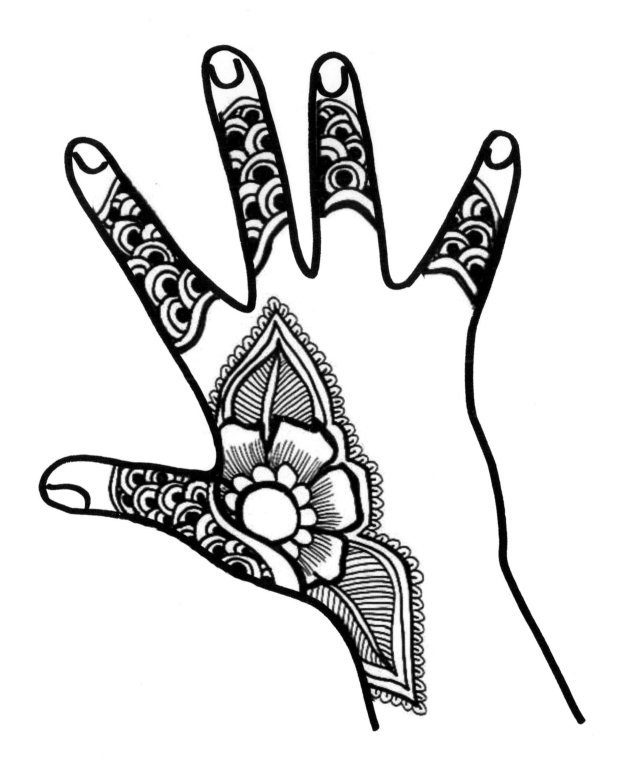

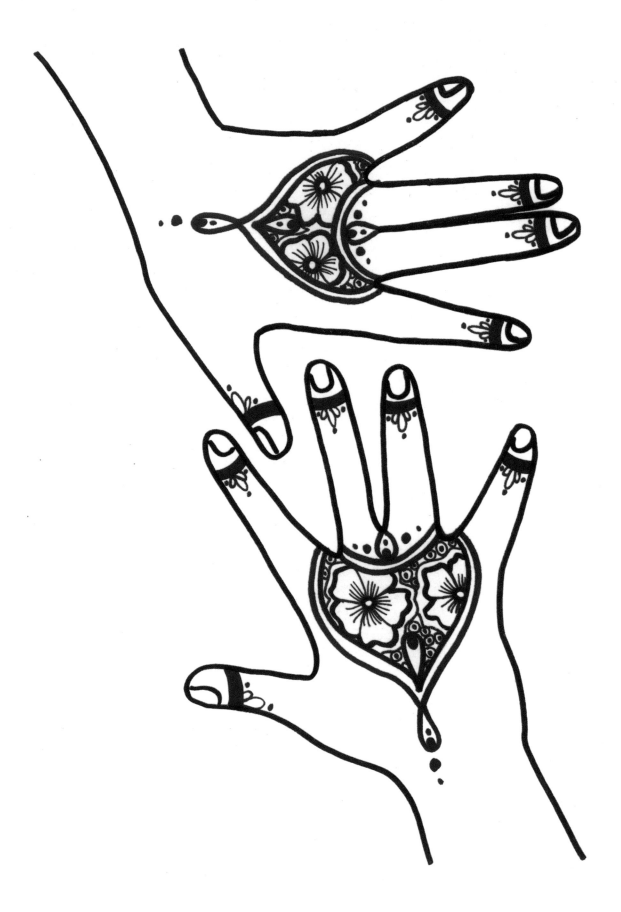

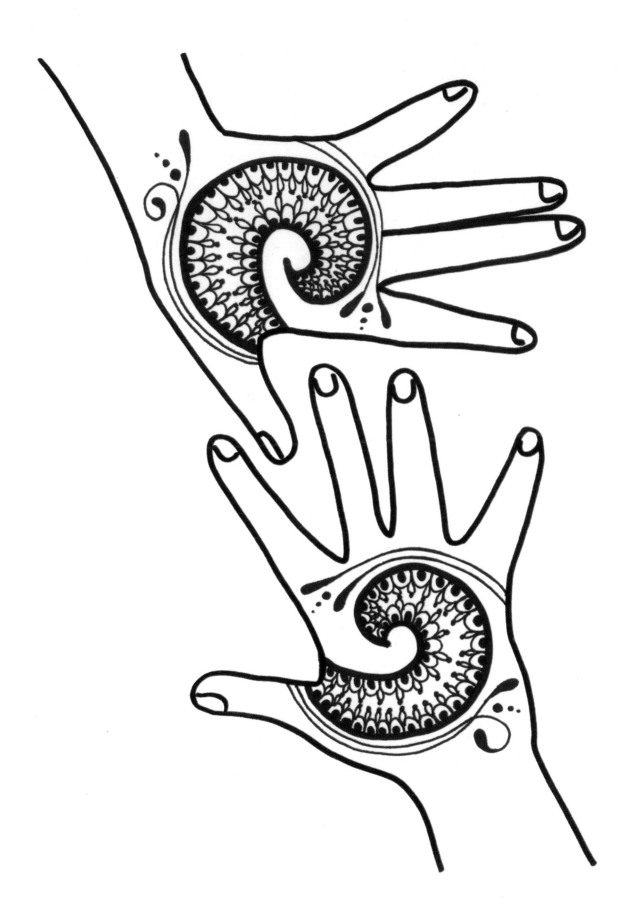

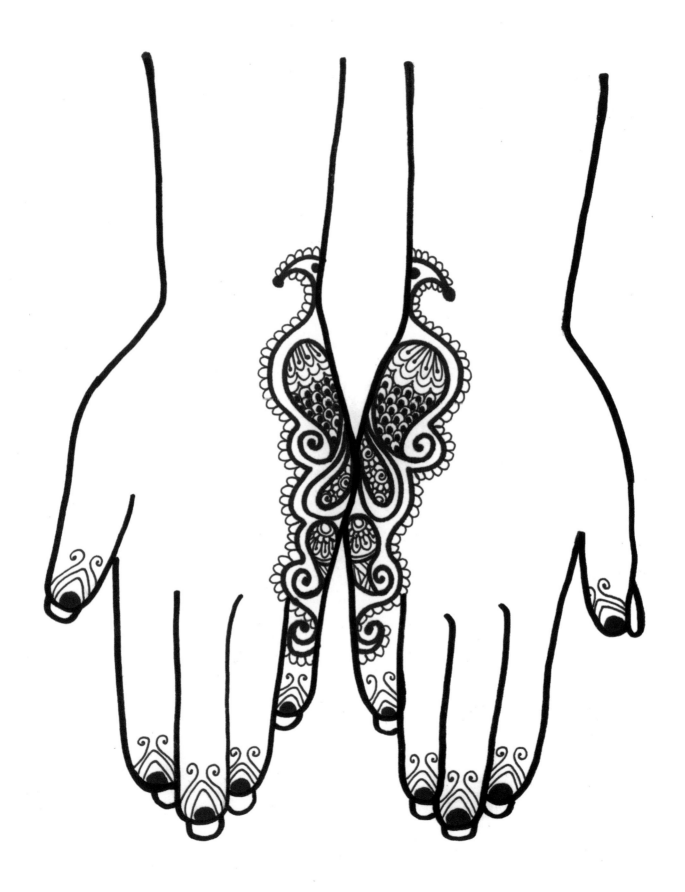

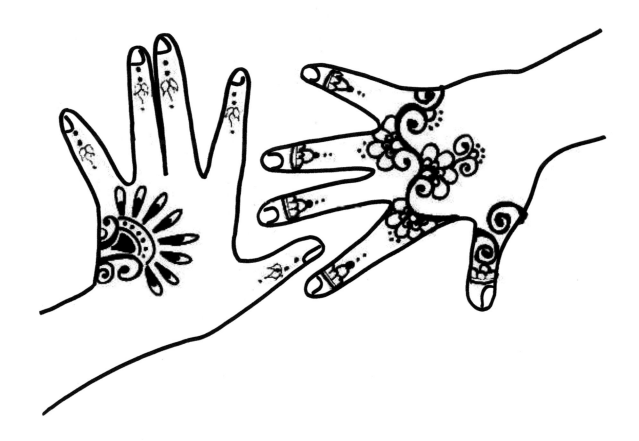

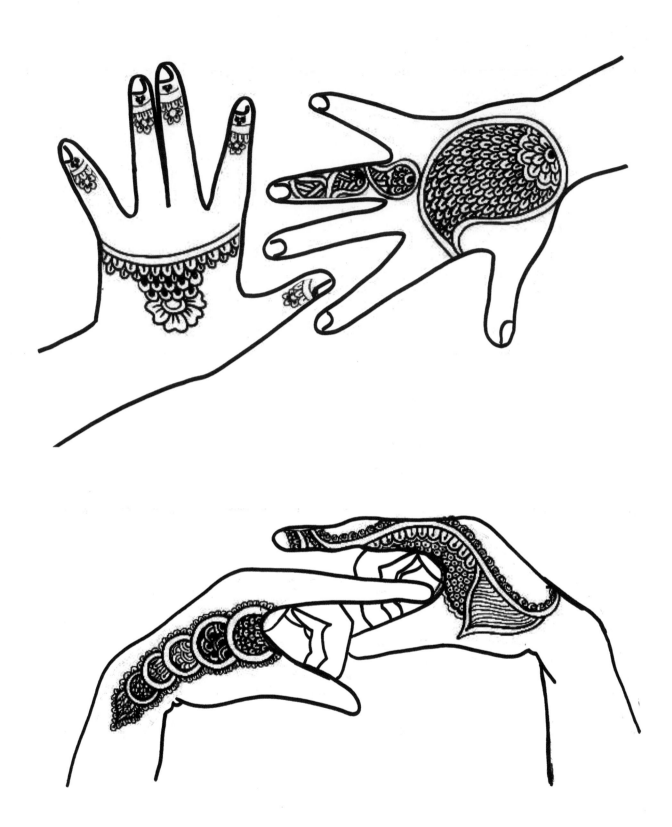

FEET

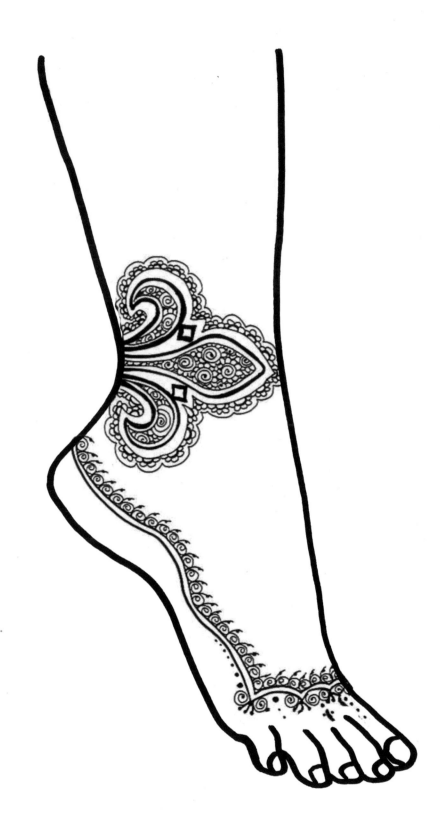

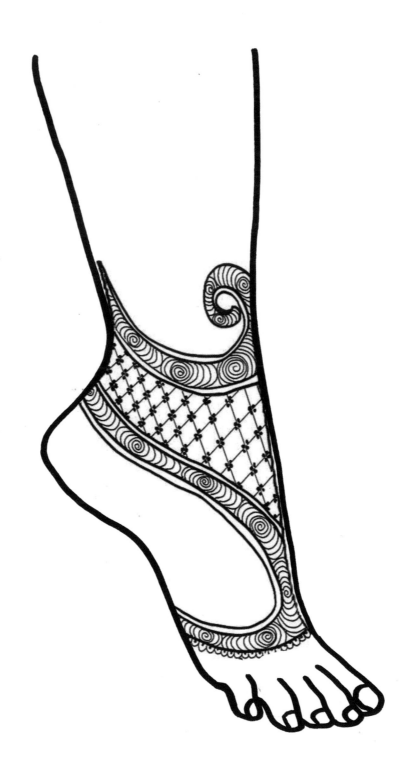

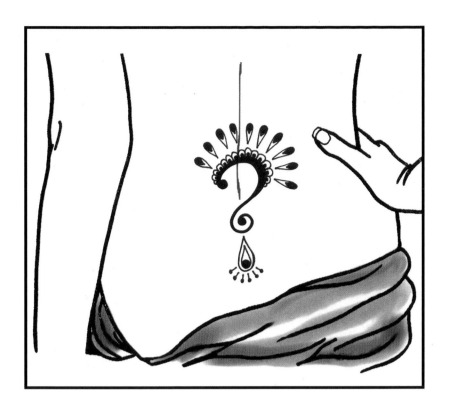

BACK

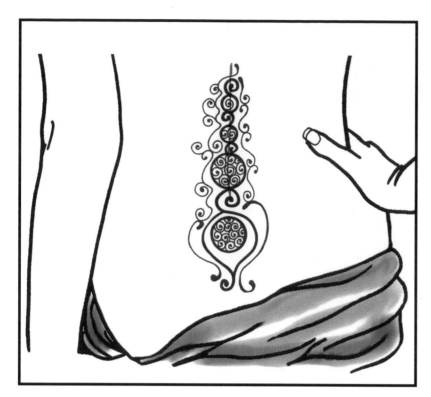

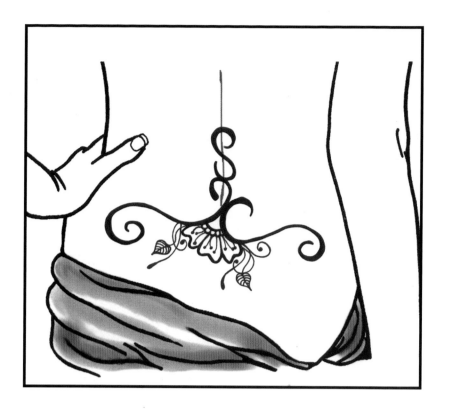

SHOULDER

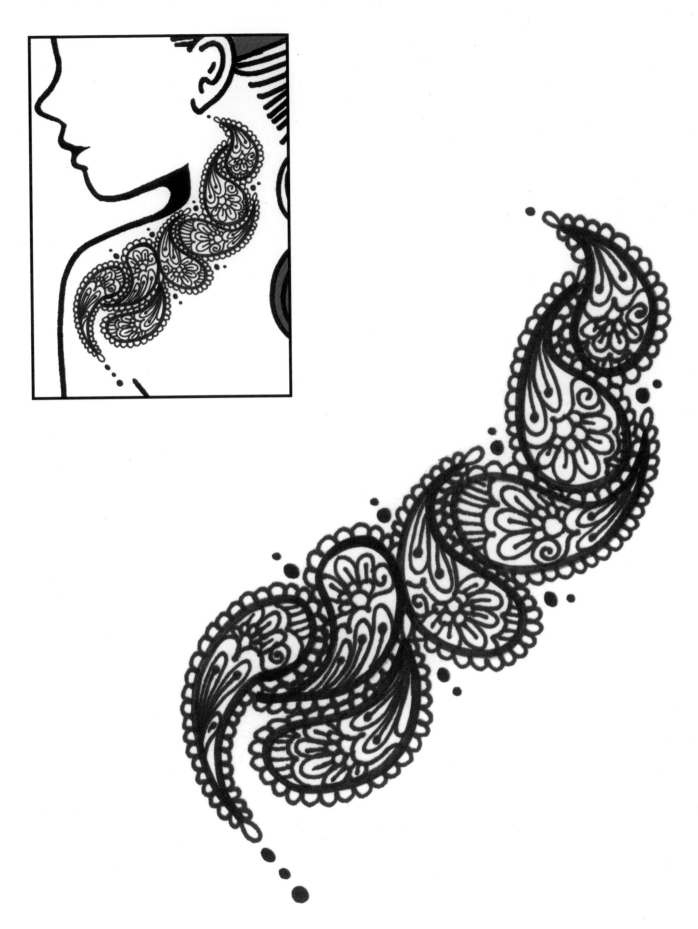

ADDITIONAL ELEMENTS

TEMPLATES

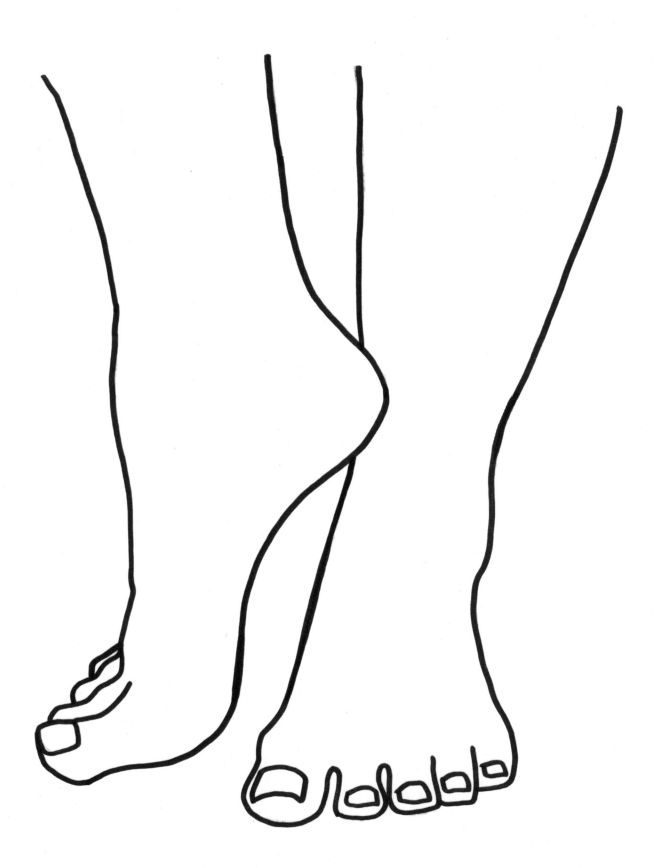

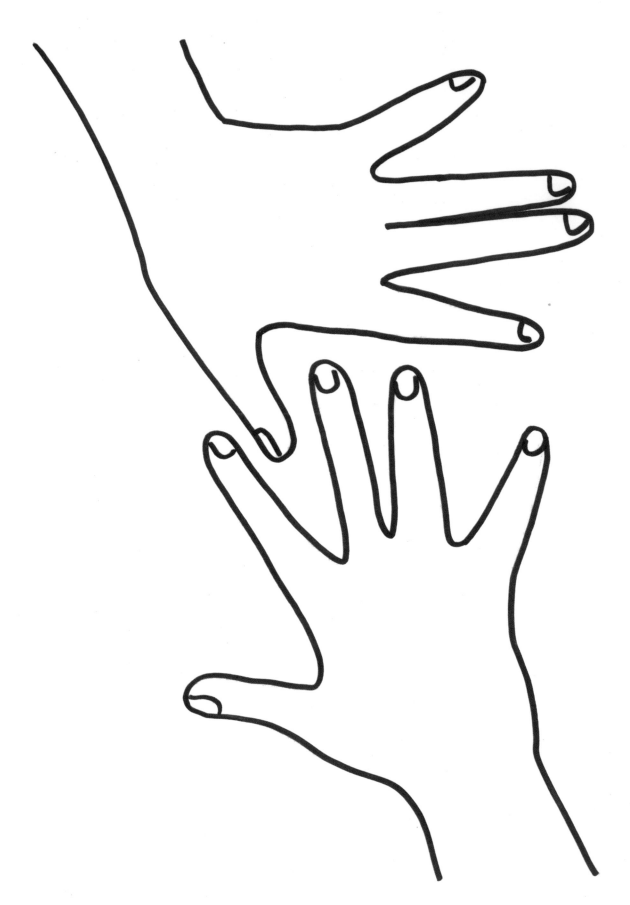

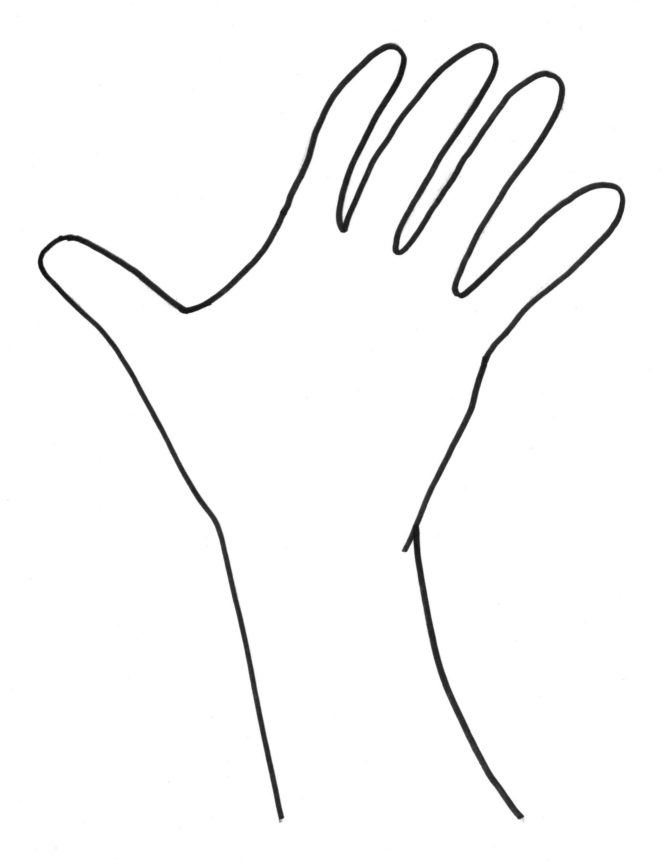

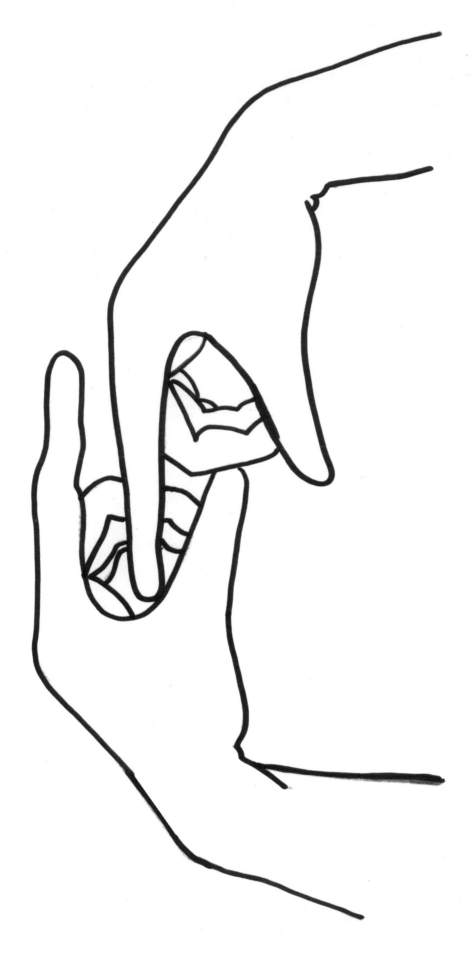

Henna as Artwork

Henna paste will stain not just skin, but also other porous, organic items. Unfinished wooden boxes and jewelry are ideal surfaces to decorate with henna tattoos. Animal skins, such as leather and the heads of drums and tambourines, also take henna stain very well. Simply apply the tattoo, let it dry, and brush it off. The design that's left behind is beautiful on its own, but you can also embellish it even more with paints, beads, and sparkling jewels.

DOING HENNA ON OBJECTS

3

Remove the dried henna paste with a blunt, hard object.

1 **Apply the henna.** Most people would describe freehand henna art as an advanced henna art skill. I do not subscribe to that belief. The same four or five basic strokes (see pages 23–25) once again come into play for henna designs on objects such as wood. However, there is one important difference: it is difficult to remove a mistake caused by misplaced henna paste on wood. Remember to allow yourself a few imperfections as you work. The handcraft of a henna artist is unique and special based on the fact that no two henna creations are alike. I suggest going with the flow and momentum of the moment. If an errant bit of henna lands somewhere unplanned, work it into your design. Other options are to touch up the area later with brown- and sepia-toned watercolor pencils or add a black border or outline with permanent marker. Whatever you do, this bit of henna work will become your original art. It will be unique, so go with it!

2 **Let the henna dry.** Once you have applied the entire design, set the object aside in a dry, out-of-the-way place so you will not accidentally bump it and smear the henna paste before it has had a chance to dry. Leave the henna paste on the wood longer than you would leave it on your skin; wood is dry, and the henna will need a little extra time to permeate the surface. I usually allow the henna paste to rest on wood for three to five days. The longer you leave it on, the deeper the color will be. Like with your skin, the surface will continue to absorb the stain and it will deepen in hue over time.

3 **Remove the paste.** When you are ready to remove the dry paste, use a blunt, hard edge of an old credit card or some other firm object to scrape the dry paste from the surface. Be careful not to press so hard that you mar or scratch the surface.

4 **Outline with marker.** If desired, you can outline the henna with a fine point, permanent black marker after removing the paste. To outline, simply follow the natural edges of your henna design. You can make the outline as thin or as thick as you like in order

4

Outlining the lines of henna give the project a whole different look.

5

Mix 2 Tbsp. water and 2 Tbsp. henna paste to form a wash.

to emphasize the intricate pattern of the henna stain on the wood surface. Because you are outlining all the edges, you will actually cover twice the amount of surface area of the henna design. This process can be time-consuming. Be patient. A slip of the wrist with permanent marker can leave a mark that might be difficult to work into your design.

5 **Apply a henna wash.** Sometimes you will want to accent parts of your design with a wash of darker color—this works best on wood. To make a henna wash, place 2 Tbsp. (30 ml) of henna paste into the small bowl with 2 Tbsp. (30 ml) of water. Stir the paste and water to create a thin henna wash that you can brush on. Apply the wash with an old paintbrush, using the same process that you would use to apply any other standard stain or paint. Allow the pieces to dry completely then rest for another 48 to 72 hours. After this waiting period, remove the henna wash, which is now a dried henna film. Use a firm-bristled toothbrush to get into the crevasses and remove all the excess henna paste.

6 **Extra touches.** For an extra glimmer, I like to apply two-dimensional paints. I use Paper Effect paints by DecoArt, which can be found in the scrapbooking section of your local craft store. Before the dimensional paint dots dry, dust the entire surface with

microfine translucent holographic glitter for maximum sparkle. Glamour Dust by DecoArt is ideal. Once the dimensional paint has dried completely, about 5 to 10 minutes, seal the entire surface with a high-gloss sealant.

7 **Apply sealant.** My personal favorite sealant is Triple Thick by DecoArt. Apply three moderate coats, allowing each coat to dry completely before proceeding to the next. For a higher shine, lightly buff each dry coat with ultrafine steel wool before applying the next coat.

Notes on working on large surfaces. Stamina, a steady hand, and specific use of all of your freehand henna art skills will be required to complete large projects. The challenge is to keep your henna strokes even and to push through the design so that all the henna is stained at as close to the same color depth as possible. If too much time elapses between one side of the project and the other, the depth of the henna stain will vary also, changing the tone from edge to edge. When I decorate a large surface, like a box, I do not hold myself to a particular plan; rather, I do random, continuous henna work until I am satisfied that the artwork is complete.

TIP When working with wood, make sure the wood is unfinished. Varnish, paint, or any kind of natural finish like linseed oil will prevent the henna from staining the wood.

This heart-shaped piece of wood was a great canvas for freehand henna. I attached a magnet to the back to add some henna to my refrigerator.

TIP When working with henna on objects, keep at least two full and ready-to-use henna cones available so you can complete the entire henna application in one go. Why? Because the faster you can apply the paste with precision, the more even the color of your design will be.

I used a peacock design on this wooden pendant. The addition of some paint and glitter really makes it pop. The challenge here was to keep the henna strokes smaller than usual.

TIP Henna paste needs to sit on the surface of wooden objects longer than on your skin to be fully absorbed. Plan for three to five days. The color will continue to deepen a bit after you remove the paste.

This tea caddy project was lots of fun; I used rhinestones and some paint dots to really accent the design.

TIPS FOR WORKING ON A BANGLE

Anchor and position the bangle blank on your non-dominant hand by threading your hand through the center of the bangle up to your knuckles. Push the bangle onto your knuckles just enough to hold it tight, but not enough to push it over onto your wrist. You could also use a Styrofoam floral cone from your local craft store. Be sure it is at least 4" in diameter at the bottom so your bangle will not fall off. A construction paper roll or the neck of a two-liter bottle are also options.

Start your design at the peak of the dome and work your way out to the rim. Try to work in a 2" x 2" (5 cm x 5 cm) space, then turn the bangle to the next 2" x 2" (5 cm x 5 cm) space and continue on around the bangle.

It is important to note that the first time you take on a project of the size and complexity of a bangle, your hands might get tired midway through. If you're working with the bangle on your knuckles, set the bangle over the bottom of an over-turned paper cup while you rest or stretch your hand so you can continue.

You may want to continue the design over the edge of the bangle and onto the inside surface. Wait at least two days until the outside is dry before you continue on the interior. If you have continued artwork to the inside, seal that with a matte sealant; gloss finishes will be less comfortable against the skin in warmer weather.

Wooden bangles are an ideal place to experiment with henna designs. Don't forget that you can decorate the inside of the bangle as well.

The henna design for this round wooden box was built around the shell at the center of the lid.

The large square surface of this wooden cigar box gives an artist an ideal space for a large repetitive and almost symmetrical design.

Henna paste dries on this wooden box. You can see how the henna decoration extends over the sides of the lid.

Color a surface before applying the henna paste to add another dimension to your artwork. This blue box was stained with colored permanent bottle inks; true paints will prevent the henna from leaving a stain.

Henna wash was used to create subtle shading between the darker lines of these henna designs on wooden boxes.

This design is a collage of henna florals, leaves, swirls, curlicues, filler dots, and circles that simply run together to create an intricate pattern of henna artwork.

You may wish to decorate the inside of the box with henna as well, or simply draw or decoupage inside.

ADDING A BEADED LEATHER LATCH

1. Decide on shape. I like making freeform latches, but you can do whatever fits your liking and project best. Cut out the leather in the shape you want for the upper (lid) and lower (box) pieces.

2. Punch for beads. If you want to have your latch edged with beads, you will need to punch holes approximately ⅛" (3mm) apart along the outer edge of your leather scraps. Do not punch the bottom edge of the lower latch.

3. Thread on the first layer of beads. Thread a length of faux sinew (long enough to whip stitch around the entire piece) through one of the holes from the bottom, slide a bead onto the sinew, then whip stitch around the outer edge of the leather and bring the thread up from the bottom through the next hole. Continue in the same manner until you run out of holes or return to the beginning. Secure the ends by knotting them and trim the tails.

4. Wire on the second layer of beads. Cut a long portion of copper 24-gauge beading wire (at least as long as the faux sinew). Thread the wire up from the back side of the first hole and through the bead already there, slide a new bead or beads on the wire, then thread the wire through the next already-laced bead. Continue until you return to your starting point. Thread the wire through the starting bead, twist the two tails together, then bend them under the bottom and toward the center of the latch piece.

5. Add third layer of beads. If desired, add a third layer of beads by repeating Step 4.

6. Thread the focal bead. Punch a small hole, just large enough for a double thickness of the faux sinew. Thread one end through the hole you punched in the center of the leather latch then thread it through your focal bead. The bead should dangle directly in front of the lower portion of the leather latch. You could add additional smaller beads to cover the excess sinew above the focal bead. You can also add charms below the focal bead (see photos on opposite page).

7. Secure the focal bead. Bring the thread back through the beads and the leather. Tie a double square knot large enough to stop the sinew from being pulled back through the hole.

8. Create the bottom latch. Punch a very small hole in the center of the lower latch. Thread a piece of copper wire through the hole and create a loop. If you want to bead the loop, do that now. Twist the tails and fold the ends to the underside.

9. Adhere the latch to the box. Place a generous portion of leather cement on the back of the latch pieces, position them where desired, and secure the leather and the box with a spring clamp or C clamp. Allow the glue to dry completely according to the manufacturer's recommendations. Before you clamp the lower latch in place, check the focal bead and loop to make sure the loop will reach over the bead. See an example of a finished beaded leather latch on page 106.

3

The first layer of beads. String beads on sinew, creating a whipstitch along the edge of the latch pieces.

4

The second layer of beads. Add another layer of decorative beads by stringing them on a smaller gauge wire.

A bold henna design, beads, and dimensional paint are
used to decorate this leather wallet.

Henna art does not need
to be limited to floral or
geometric designs.

A spherical surface like this round wooden ball gives the artist an ideal canvas for a continuous repetitive design.

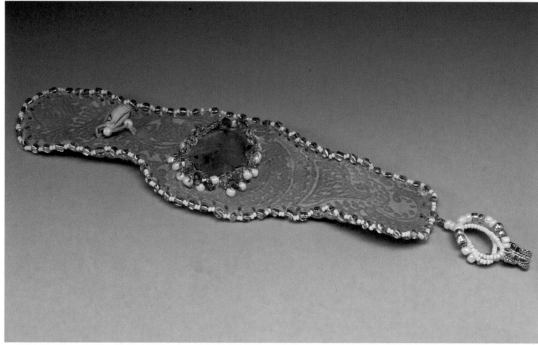

Henna paste will also stain leather used for jewelry and clothing. A loop of smaller beads and a larger bead fastened directly to the leather create a clasp.

RESOURCES

SUPPLIES

HENNA POWDER
www.beachcombersbazaar.com
www.thehennapage.com

JAC BOTTLES
www.beachcombersbazaar.com
www.thehennapage.com
www.JacquardProducts.com

ESSENTIAL OILS (TEA TREE AND OTHERS)
www.beachcombersbazaar.com
www.thehennapage.com

READY-MADE MYLAR CONES
www.thehennapage.com

BAJIDOO HOW-TO VIDEOS
www.youtube.com/user/babdoyan

BRENDA ABDOYAN, BAJIDOO, INC.
www.bajidoo.com
www.brendaabdoyan.net

HAVE MORE QUESTIONS?
info@bajidoo.com or *abdoyan@bajidoo.com*

INDEX

Acquisition Editor: Peg Couch

Cover and Page Designer: Lindsay Hess

Developmental Editor: Ayleen Stellhorn

Editor: Kerri Landis

Layout Designer: Ashley Millhouse

Proofreader: Lisa Caylor

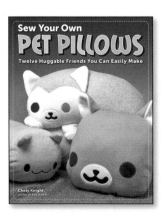